RUNNING

RUNNING
training • motivation • performance • nutrition

RACHEL NEWCOMBE

Bath · New York · Singapore · Hong Kong · Cologne · Delhi · Melbourne

First published by Parragon in 2008

Parragon
Queen Street House
4 Queen Street
Bath BA1 1HE, UK

ISBN 978-1-4075-1767-4
Printed in Malaysia

Produced by the Bridgewater Book Company Ltd
Photography: Ian Parsons
Hair and makeup stylist: Hannah Deacon
Models: Charlotte Curtis and Will Bligh
Consultant: Sam Lambourne
Cover images: Corbis/Cory Sorensen and Tim Tadder

The publisher would like to thank The Jog Shop, Brighton,
England, for the use of their equipment.

NOTE FOR THE READER
The views expressed in this book are those of the author,
but are general views and intended as a guide only. Readers
are urged to consult a relevant and qualified practitioner for
specialized and tailored advice. Appropriate independent
advice should be obtained from a medical practitioner
before carrying out any exercise, especially if you haven't
exercised before.

CONTENTS

INTRODUCTION

Running is one of the most popular forms of exercise you can choose. Almost anyone can take part and, unlike many sports, it doesn't require a great deal of expensive equipment. If you would like to get into shape, manage your weight, or lose some extra pounds, or if you just want to try a different form of exercise, running could be the answer you're looking for.

People have always had good reason to run: in times of hunting and warfare, running was often a matter of life and death. It is not known exactly when running made the transition to a sport, but there are indications that the Egyptians took part in races as early as 3,800 BCE. At the very first ancient Olympics, sprinting was the only race, although many more running events were added subsequently.

Today, running is still a key element of the Olympic Games. What's more, running is practiced for fun and fitness purposes all over the world. At any time of day, there are joggers out on the streets and in our neighborhood parks, and there are numerous running clubs. Marathons, fun runs, and charity running events are regular fixtures in the calendar, encouraging more and more people to get up and try the sport. If you are similarly inspired, but are not sure how to get started, then this is the book for you.

Your introduction to running

This book focuses on the art of running, taking you through all you need to know to get started and continue to improve. It will prepare you for your first trip on the road or on the treadmill, guide you through the key items of equipment, such as running shoes, and explain how you can monitor your increasing fitness. It covers food, fluid intake, and nutrition, and also explains common running injuries and how you can prevent them.

You'll find it a handy guide to help you through your first few weeks of running, plus you'll find hints, tips, and step-by-step instructions on how to warm up, stretch, and cool down safely. The book also covers cross training and suggests exercises to work your nonrunning muscles so that you can develop an all-round great level of fitness.

The third chapter, Advanced Training, takes you to the next level by examining the various opportunities available for runners who want to take part in charity runs or competitive races. One of the main concerns of runners is how much training they should do, and the final chapter deals with this and provides a selection of sample training programs. Beginners are offered guidance on how to build up their running after they've completed their first training schedule, and there are plenty of suggestions for intermediates who want to try runs of 5,000 m (3.1 miles) and 10,000 m (6.2 miles) , or even think about training for a marathon.

It doesn't matter if you have not run since you were a child or do not do much exercise at the moment.

With this book, you are not going to be left to struggle through 10,000 m without any prior training. Instead, we take a slow approach, encouraging you to build up your activity gradually each week. When you start running as a sport for the first time, it's not a good idea to run for the entire session, and we mix these early training sessions with timed periods of walking.

Designed to be your companion in the early days, and a useful guide as you improve, this book provides you with a thorough grounding, so that you can be sure of a successful start to your running practice, from which you can develop, hone, and improve your skills.

1

Getting Started

Running brings with it numerous benefits—not least improved health and fitness—and it can be a sociable hobby. This section provides you with all you need to know about getting started, from monitoring your fitness and preventing injuries, to the types of running shoes, clothing, and equipment available.

WHY GET INTO RUNNING?

Of all sports and forms of exercise, running is one of the easiest and most accessible. It doesn't involve a wide array of expensive equipment, you don't need to spend excessive amounts of time or money learning how to do it, and you don't need to travel to a specially designated location. Anyone, anywhere, who is willing to give it a go, can try running.

What running can do for you

Running provides a wide variety of physical, mental, and social benefits and you can tap into these at any level. Exercise is one of the best ways of boosting your health and fitness, and running can help reduce your risk of developing a range of debilitating conditions, including heart problems, osteoporosis, arthritis, high blood pressure, and diabetes.

As an excellent form of aerobic activity, running is also one of the best exercises you can commit to if you want to manage your weight or keep in shape. For about every half mile you run, you can expect to burn around 100 calories. Running will help you reduce body fat and tone up your muscles so they become leaner and fitter. It may also have a positive impact on your sleeping patterns, because regular exercise can improve sleep.

If you run regularly, you will also build up your strength, and this will give you more energy, so that you can cope better with the demands of life. Many people gain a sense of accomplishment from running—even in the early stages when progress can seem slow—and in turn this feeling boosts self-esteem and confidence.

Believe it or not, running will also help you relax and, if you are feeling stressed, running provides you with an effective tool to manage it.

Running for fun

You may not think of running as a social sport, but if you want it to be, it can be. Some runners are happy to run on their own and stick to their own schedules, but if you're interested in gaining support, sharing tips, and advice or just training with other people, there are many

opportunities for engaging in the social side. Running is a popular sport and numerous running clubs exist, enabling you to run in a large group or to run alongside others who are at the same level as you. Clubs usually cater for all abilities, whether you're completely new to running or have been running for years, and they organize set times and routes for running, as well as regular social events. The advice, support, and tips you pick up from people who've been running for a while can be invaluable. Clubs are a useful source of local information, too, and you'll discover where it is and isn't advisable to run in your local vicinity.

Racing

For beginners, simply learning to run, maintaining the habit, and slowly improving can be enough. But as you progress, you may want to advance more and there are plenty of opportunities out there. Taking part in races, whether for competitive purposes, the pure joy of it or to

raise money for charity, can be enormously rewarding. Runs of 5,000 m and 10,000 m (3.1 and 6.2 miles) are especially popular with most runners. Many charities now organize annual fundraising runs, which help promote the benefits of getting fit and participating in running, while at the same time raising funds for valuable work.

Anyone who is seriously committed to running and in search of a challenge could set their sights on one of the big-name annual marathons. These international events are held in many countries around the world and include the famous New York and London Marathons.

tip *Running will make you feel better mentally as well as physically. This is because when you exercise the brain produces endorphins, which act by blocking pain receptors. It is believed that they help create a natural high, which results in you feeling good.*

MAKING RUNNING PART OF YOUR LIFE

If you take up running regularly, it will soon begin to impact on other areas of your life. You may find that you need to make a few changes to your lifestyle, or it may affect your habits in ways that you hadn't expected. Stick with it and you can be sure that running will boost your overall well-being and that any changes made will be for the better.

You may, for example, become more aware of what you're eating and what effect it is having on your body. You may be tempted into other types of exercise—even if it just means being more ready to run for a bus—or you may want to review "bad" habits, such as smoking, or drinking too much. As running becomes a part of your life, you will become more aware of your health and level of fitness, and this will lead naturally to tweaks to your overall lifestyle.

Making a schedule

Now is the time to consider what days and times you're going to run, how far you'll go, and what you need to do to achieve this. It's helpful to identify set times, as many times a week as is realistic, that you'll dedicate to running, so you have a schedule and can plan ahead around it. Finding times to suit you will depend on several factors, such as when you're working, looking after the family or engaged in other long-standing commitments—arriving at a schedule can be a challenge in itself. This preplanning is well worth it, however, because it will enable you to keep disciplined and will ensure you've allotted your running practice the time it needs.

Don't forget that running can, to some extent, be fitted in around your existing plans. Do you have some spare time in the morning before work, in your lunch hour, or in the evenings? If you're a beginner, it's best not to run for long periods of time, so short runs of 20, 30, or 40 minutes may be all you need. Juggle your schedule as much as you can to find the best time for

you. Once you've decided when you're going to run, let other people, or at least your family, know, too, so that they will be aware that you won't be available during those times.

Mental preparation

Self-discipline and motivation are essential, perhaps especially so in the early days. Progress will probably be slow at first and there will be times when you will feel disappointed and frustrated that you aren't able to run far without feeling tired. There will even be days when you feel like giving up and watching television instead. Don't lose heart!

Once you've built up your strength and stamina, running will become easier. You'll be able to run for longer, cover more distance, and achieve a faster pace. Eventually you will be able to keep up with more experienced runners instead of being left behind. The trick is not to expect instant results but to allow your body to improve gradually.

Try to adopt a positive outlook and think positive thoughts. When a negative thought such as, "No, I can't do it!" enters your mind, shoo it away with a positive thought such as, "It's a challenge, but I know I can overcome it." If you need an little extra incentive, keep positive quotes on your desk or stuck on the refrigerator, reminding yourself that running makes you feel good and you do want to stick with it.

tip *To help combat the self-doubt and worries that may occur, think ahead and use visualization to focus on your running goals. Imagine yourself, for example, crossing the finishing line of your first competition run.*

BODY TYPES

Although we are all different, people generally fall into one of three basic body types—endomorph, mesomorph, or ectomorph. Not everyone fits exactly into one type, and you may combine elements of two, but there are likely to be qualities of one type that are predominant. Finding out which body type best describes you can be helpful, because each body type has its own characteristics and ways it responds to exercise and diet.

Endomorph

If you are an endomorph, your body will tend to be pearshaped, so that your hips are broader than your shoulders and you have a wide bone structure. You're also more likely to have a curvier body than other types, and may be prone to gaining weight and storing fat. Running and other forms of aerobic activity are good methods for controlling this.

Mesomorph

If you are a mesomorph, then you're likely to be of average weight—neither plump nor skinny—and have a shape that falls somewhere between endomorph and ectomorph. Your shoulders may be wider than your hips and you may have a tendency to gain muscle easily, but you'll generally have little in the way of body fat. You'll also find it relatively easy to lose weight. A balanced running program, which includes a variety of cross-training activities (see page 62) is a good option for mesomorphs, because it will ensure the whole body is being exercised.

Ectomorph

Typical ectomorphs are thin and have a small frame. Your shoulders and hips will be narrow, you'll have very

APPLES AND PEARS

Use the following technique to discover whether you're more of an apple than a pear. You're appleshaped if the ratio is 0.8 or more for women and 1.0 or more for men. If the ratio is less than 0.8 or 1.0, you have more of a pear shape.

1 Place a tape measure directly onto your skin (not over clothes) and measure your waist at the navel and your hips at their widest point.

2 To work out your waist to hip ratio, divide the waist measurement by the hip measurement. The result will be your waist to hip ratio.

Of course, you may have a neutral body shape that's neither apple- or pearlike. If this sounds like you, then stick to a good running routine, eat a healthy balanced diet, and enjoy your choice of cross training.

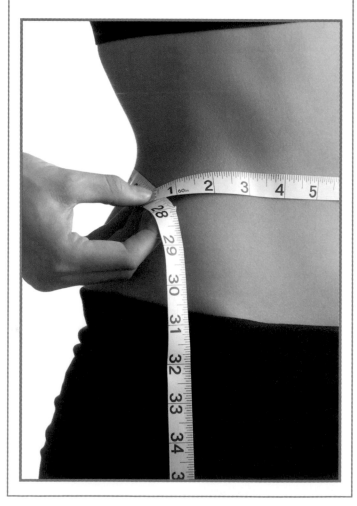

little in the way of body fat, and a narrow chest and stomach. Your legs and arms will also be thin and you will have a narrow face with a high forehead.

Ectomorphs tend to flourish with running. However, this body type can be prone to fatigue and it's important not to attempt to run when you're tired or haven't recovered sufficiently from a previous run.

Apple and pear

You may have come across the terms apple and pear to describe body shapes. If you're an apple, then you tend to gain fat in the mid section of the body—the stomach, chest, and abdomen. Running is a great form of exercise for apple shapes because it can help burn fat and decrease the storage of fat around the waist. Combine it with cross-training routines for improved health.

People with pearshaped bodies tend to store fat below the waistline. Although it's regarded as healthier to be pearshaped than appleshaped, the thighs, buttocks, and hips may need extra attention to keep them in shape. Stretching exercises that focus on these areas will be doubly important.

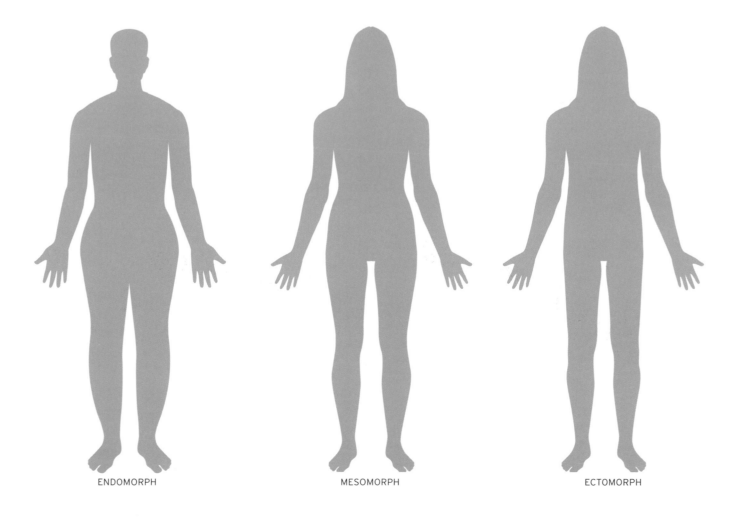

ENDOMORPH   MESOMORPH   ECTOMORPH

ASSESSING YOUR LEVEL OF FITNESS

Before you start running, it's advisable to think about and assess your current level of fitness. Although it's possible to do this on your own, getting advice from a medical expert or fitness instructor can also be valuable.

If you've not exercised for a while, have had or have a medical complaint, or have never run, it's advisable to see a doctor before you embark on a running regimen. Book an appointment for a medical check and to discuss your health. Apart from ensuring that your health is currently good and that you don't have any issues you're unaware of, this will also provide you with the reassurance that you can start running without expecting any problems. Once you've been given the all clear, you can draw up a schedule, identify your initial goals, and purchase any equipment you need.

Your resting heart rate
As well as getting checked over by a medical professional, one of the best and easiest ways of establishing how fit you are is to find out what your resting heart rate is. To do this, you need to take your pulse when you're not doing exercise. First thing in the morning, when you've just woken up but haven't properly got up yet, is an ideal time.

To help assess and monitor your fitness over time and see what impact the running you're doing is having on your heart, make a point of taking your resting heart rate regularly. Knowing what it is and seeing the positive changes can be a useful motivating tool. Why not keep a log or plot the figures on a chart? If your running practice isn't going as well as you'd like, or you can't muster up the energy to go out, you can look back on your heart rate figures to remind yourself of the progress you've made.

Gym assessment

Another way to establish how fit you are is to undergo a fitness check with an instructor at a local health club. This can provide a useful overview of your current fitness level and highlight any areas that need particular work. The exact format varies, but should include a questionnaire about your health, discussion about how much exercise you currently do, and a series of simple tests to assess your cardiovascular health and your overall strength and flexibility. One test that may be used, for example, is the "bleep test", where you run a series of set distances in the times set by two audible bleeps.

At the end of your assessment, you may receive your fitness scores, which can be used as a benchmark for aiding improvement. The instructor may also be able to provide some helpful hints and tips, based on your individual health and fitness level, on how to begin your running program, and what you should be aiming to achieve.

WHAT'S YOUR RESTING HEART RATE?

Take your pulse by either placing two fingers on your neck, just below your jawbone, or on your wrist. Use a stopwatch or watch and count the number of times your pulse beats in 10 seconds. Multiply this figure by six to calculate the number of times your pulse beats in a minute. The figure you have is your resting heart rate. For most people, this figure lies between 60 and 80, but the fitter you become and the stronger your heart gets, the lower your resting heart rate will be. Everyone's resting heart rate differs—some forms of medication can increase it and it will be higher if you're unfit or haven't exercised for a while. If you are concerned about the reading you get, speak to your doctor.

tip *Your resting heart rate may increase naturally as you get older. If it appears to get higher suddenly, after a period of extensive training, this may be an indication that you're pushing yourself too hard and need to slow down your pace or reduce the frequency of your runs.*

MONITORING YOUR FITNESS LEVEL

Your heart rate—the number of times per minute that your heart pumps blood throughout your body—is a good indicator of your level of cardiovascular fitness. By using a heart rate monitor (HRM), you can track what your heart rate is when you exercise, gauge how hard you are training, and find out whether you need to increase or decrease your pace.

A heart rate monitor comes in two parts. A strap with sensors on it is worn around your chest and a receiver, which picks up your heart rate signals, is worn on your wrist like a watch. Various models are available with different functions and abilities; your monitor might, for example, tell you your heart-rate recovery time, how many calories you've burned, and whether you're in your upper or lower heart-rate target limits. The price of monitors has dropped in recent years and you can pick up an inexpensive model. When you're buying, check the functions carefully, because they will vary.

Maximum heart rate

The key to programming and using a heart rate monitor successfully is to know your maximum heart rate (MHR). You can calculate this by deducting your age from 220 if you are male, and 226 if you are female. So, if you're 40 years old, your maximum heart rate is 180 beats per minute if you are male and 186 if you are female. To push yourself over your MHR is dangerous, because it places intolerable strain on your body. You can use your MHR to help build your training program.

For beginners, the optimum training zone is about 60-70 percent of your MHR. At this level, your body will be exercising efficiently and getting fitter. What's more, you can rest assured that by keeping to this level you won't be overtraining or exhausting yourself. Start slowly and aim for the bottom of your target, 60 percent, and build up gradually. You can program your MHR into the heart rate monitor and it will cleverly track your progress for you, which can be very rewarding feedback.

Setting goals and targets

Many runners, whatever their level of ability, find it helpful to set goals and targets. For beginners, this might be to run for 10 minutes without stopping, or to run a set distance in a slightly shorter time. Other common goals include losing weight through running, building up fitness, or improving enough to take part in an organized run or race.

Having a goal can help keep you motivated and focused. There are bound to be days when your running attempts don't go so well, or you don't feel like braving

the elements and going outside. Or perhaps you feel unwell for a week or so and your fitness level slips back a notch. At times like this, goals can be a real lifesaver, giving you the motivation to keep going when it would be easy to give up.

It can help to conjure up images of what it will be like to achieve your goal and how you'll feel when you get there. Keep these thoughts in mind as you train, reminding yourself of them when things get tough. Also, think about how you might celebrate or reward yourself when you achieve your target, so that you've got something extra to look forward to.

If you want to keep your goal, or goals, to yourself, that's fine. But if you're happy to share your dreams with other people, they will probably encourage you to meet the challenge, and their involvement can be a useful motivating factor.

tip *When you're setting a target or goal, make sure it's something that will challenge you, but that will be achievable in the short term. It could be one goal, or several. Long-term goals can work, too, but are usually best placed alongside short-term goals, because they may otherwise seem too impossibly far off to achieve.*

NUTRITION

Eating a healthy balanced diet is something we should all aim for and, for runners, it's especially important because exercising puts extra demands on your body.

Carbohydrates, fruits, and vegetables should make up the bulk of your diet, followed by milk and dairy foods, and meat, fish, and alternatives. Foods containing saturated fats and sugar should be kept to a minimum. However, unsaturated (monounsaturated and polyunsaturated) fats are important. They supply fat-soluble vitamins, such as A, D, E, and K. Olive oil is a good source of monounsaturated fat and polyunsaturates omega-3 and omega-6 are found in sunflower oil, linseed, and oily fish. The most important food group for runners is carbohydrates. They are an ideal source of fuel for running and provide the body with essential B vitamins that play a role in boosting energy, and fiber, which helps clear the system. Carbohydrates are referred to as fuel because, when consumed, they're converted into glycogen—a substance that is burned quickly and easily.

The body can only store a limited amount of glycogen, so a balanced diet helps replenish stores. One bonus of becoming a better runner is that as you become fitter it will become easier for your body to store glycogen. It's worth noting that if you've run or trained for a long time in one session, it's recommended you eat within two hours of finishing, because this helps replace the glycogen and speed up recovery.

Foods rich in protein, such as meat, fish, and legumes, are also important for runners because proteins are involved in building muscles. Dairy foods are rich in calcium, which helps build strong bones and reduce the risk of fractures. Try to eat a wide range of fruits and vegetables of various colors. They are packed with essential vitamins and minerals, including antioxidants, such as A, C, and E. Fresh produce is great, but dried, frozen, and canned are all good to incorporate, too.

As far as quantities of food go, if you continue to eat the same amount as you did before you started running, then you'll lose weight—running burns about 100 calories per half mile (1 km). If you don't want to lose weight, you'll need to eat and drink more—but choose healthy foods!

Eating as a runner

If you're planning to go running first thing in the morning, try not to do so on an empty stomach. It doesn't have to be a big breakfast, but something light, such as a piece of toast or a banana, eaten about half an hour before you set off, will provide the energy that your body needs after a long sleep.

One downside of running and exercise in general is that it can increase the production of free radicals—molecules that cause harm to healthy cells. To combat

ESSENTIAL FOOD GROUPS

To maintain a healthy diet you need to eat foods from the five main food groups:

Bread, cereals, and potatoes (carbohydrates)

Fruits and vegetables

Milk and dairy foods

Meat, fish, and alternatives (proteins)

Foods containing fat or sugar

this, include plenty of foods rich in antioxidants in your diet, because they fight free radicals. Examples of antioxidant-rich foods include oranges, strawberries, broccoli, tomatoes, carrots, and spinach.

As you progress with your running, you may need to experiment with the amount of food you eat (you'll be burning off more calories) and what foods work best before runs. One useful way of assessing this is to keep a log of what you eat for a few weeks. Alongside the list of food consumed, note how you felt when running. Did you have plenty of energy, did you have stomach cramps, or did you feel too full? Your log may not highlight any issues, but if it does, you can pinpoint the culprit foods or actions and make positive changes to amend them.

tip *Bananas are a good source of carbohydrates and vitamin B6 and can be eaten on the move.*

HYDRATION

Water makes up about 60 percent of your total body weight and performs a range of crucial functions. It helps regulate your body temperature, provides nourishment to cells, aids the elimination of waste, helps maintain blood pressure, and helps lubricate the joints. If you don't drink enough water, it will have an adverse effect on your health, including a heightened risk of urinary tract infections and kidney stones.

It's clear that everyone should ensure they drink plenty of water each day, but it's even more important if you're running or exercising in any other way. When you run your body temperature increases. Heat is produced in the muscles as calories are burned and the rise in temperature triggers the need for the body to sweat.

The act of sweating helps the body cool down. Sweating causes loss of fluid and, if this fluid is not subsequently replaced, can lead to dehydration.

Not everyone sweats to the same degree when they run and it's governed by a range of factors. The exterior temperature plays a part, because the hotter it is, the more you sweat. If the weather is windy, the wind can help cool the body and reduce our need to sweat so much. Women tend to sweat less than men, and how much you sweat also depends in part on your individual genetic makeup.

One way of gauging if you're drinking enough water, or if you're dehydrated, is to check your urine. If you've been drinking enough, it will be clear or pale and odorless, but if you're dehydrated it will be darker and may smell. Other signs that you may be dehydrated include headaches, fatigue, and generally feeling weak.

Developing good habits

Getting into good drinking habits will help your health in general, as well as aid your running performance. Aim to drink between six and eight 8-fl oz (225-ml) glasses of water throughout the day, at regular intervals; that's the equivalent of about 8 cups (2 liters). If you wait until you're thirsty to drink, your body is already dehydrated.

Be aware that tea and coffee, as well as soft drinks such as cola, contain caffeine and can increase dehydration. There's no need to avoid them, but if you are planning to go out running soon after drinking them, have a glass of water to make sure you're fully hydrated.

When you're out on a run, either take a bottle of water with you (a small backpack with a small bottle of water in shouldn't be too heavy) or try to plan your route so there will be somewhere to stop for water.

WHICH SPORTS DRINK?

Isotonic drinks contain carbohydrate particles and sometimes electrolytes. They may help replace lost minerals and boost energy levels, especially when they contain glucose. The concentration is the same as the body's own fluids, which means they are absorbed into the bloodstream at the same rate as water.

Hypotonic drinks are good to consume during a race. They are more quickly absorbed by the body as they contain particles that are less concentrated than those of body fluid. They may also help increase the rate at which water is absorbed.

Hypertonic drinks are absorbed more slowly and are best consumed as a recovery drink or an energy booster after you've finished a run.

Sports drinks

Energy drinks are now widely available and are a good supplement to water. They're designed for people who are exercising and the balance of ingredients ensures that the fluid is absorbed by the body faster than water or fruit juices alone. There are various types of sports drinks, including isotonic, hypotonic, and hypertonic.

If you're going for a short run in cool weather, then water should be sufficient for restoring fluid levels. However if you're training, running, or exercising for a long period, or in warm conditions, an energy drink is a far better option. As a guide, for each hour you exercise consume 14–24 fl oz (400–700 ml) of an isotonic or hypotonic drink. Have about 14 fl oz (400 ml) before you train, then regular sips every 15 minutes while exercising. Alternatively, if you find it difficult to drink while running, drink more at the end of your session.

tip *You can derive valuable fluid from foods, such as tomatoes, cucumber, lettuce, oranges, and bananas.*

INJURY PREVENTION

No one wants an injury, but running as a sport can sometimes cause unwanted ailments. While some types of injury are hard to predict, others are more common and there are practical methods you can employ to reduce your risk of having one.

Making sure you warm up before running plays an important role in reducing the risk of injuries occurring. Warming up helps your muscles become more flexible and supple, reducing tightness and limbering them up ready for the exercise that lies ahead. If you skip the warm up, your muscles will remain tight and injuries are more likely to occur. Likewise, after your run, taking time to cool down also reduces your injury risk.

It's equally important to ensure you recover fully after each session before going out again. Going from no running to training every day will ultimately wear your body out—even more experienced runners don't necessarily train every day—so pace yourself and ease into a sensible running routine. If you do a long or hard run on one session, make the next one shorter and easier, so your body has time to recover. If you're feeling under par, tired, or unwell, don't push yourself to run.

STRENGTHENING THE KNEES

The knees take some battering when running, and knee pain and injuries are common. You can strengthen your knee muscles, and subsequently reduce the risk of injuries, by performing regular leg exercises, such as this one. Sit upright on a chair with your back straight, your hands beside you, and your feet resting flat on the floor. Slowly lift your right leg straight out in front of you, then hold the position for 10 seconds. Repeat this exercise twice on each leg.

CAUTION!

If you've had an injury, follow the advice of your medical practitioner about how long you should wait before going back to running. However keen you are to get back out, it's not worth the risk of exacerbating the injury.

Common injuries

Running injuries typically affect the feet, ankles, back, hips, knees, and shins and include conditions, such as muscle sprains and strains, Achilles tendonitis, back pain, sciatica, muscle soreness, and stress fractures.

It's not surprising that the feet commonly develop from injuries, since they take a pounding when you run. One cause of sprained ankles is tripping or misplacing your feet. It's easily done, but try to watch out for cracks or bumps in the sidewalk or road, and be careful if you're in areas where there might be exposed tree roots. Wearing inappropriate shoes can also play a part in causing foot injuries, as can failing to replace running shoes that are worn out.

Other minor foot complaints include blisters, bunions, ingrowing toenails, and fungal infections, and they can all make running uncomfortable. You can help prevent blisters by putting petroleum jelly or a heavy moisturizing cream on your feet before running, because this acts as a kind of barrier. Ingrowing toenails can be prevented by cutting nails straight across, and the risk of fungal infections can be reduced by keeping your feet as dry as possible.

Shin splints is a term used to describe the experience of pain shooting up and down the front of the lower leg. The exact cause isn't known, but it's believed to be related to suddenly increasing the amount and level of running you do. It can be painful, but keeping to a balanced running schedule may prevent this condition from occurring.

If you do have any injuries, it's advisable to get them checked out by a doctor, instead of trying to self-diagnose. Your injuries may be minor, but when you're starting out and aren't familiar with the strains and pains caused by running, expert advice is valuable. If your injury is more serious, delaying diagnosis and treatment could slow down recovery.

EQUIPMENT

A good pair of running shoes is your most crucial piece of equipment. Statistics suggest that for every mile you run, your feet strike the ground about 800 times. Both your shoes and your feet absorb the impact shock and it subsequently ricochets up your legs and into the rest of your body. If you don't have adequate shoes, then it could lead to a range of injuries.

Don't just buy the first pair of cheap sneakers you see in a store because they're unlikely to be suitable for running. Tennis, aerobics, or cross-training shoes are not up to the job. Instead, head straight to a specialized running store to buy your running shoes, because they'll be able to provide expert advice on the right shoes for you. Try on plenty of different options to find the most

comfortable. If you're buying a replacement or second pair, take along your old shoes—however old or worn—because they will help the store staff to assess your running style and which type of shoes would suit you. Some specialist stores offer a very helpful "try before you buy" service, where you can go for a test run before making a purchase. This is a valuable way to assess the fit of a pair of shoes while running.

Time it right

Try to avoid shopping for running shoes first thing in the morning. The best time to go is in the afternoon, when you've been up and about and walking around for a while. Feet naturally swell during the day and also when you're running, so this will provide a more accurate impression of your feet. Remember to take along the socks you wear for running, too, so you can make sure your socked feet fit comfortably in the shoes.

A good sales assistant in a specialist store will probably ask questions about how long you've been running, what surfaces you run on, and how far you usually run, so be prepared to answer them. Your answers will assist them in advising you on the most appropriate shoes for you. Don't be afraid to ask questions yourself if you're unsure of anything, and ensure you specify a budget if you have one.

An ideal running shoe should fit comfortably, but not feel too tight. There should still be room at the front of the shoe for your toes to move around and the heel should fit snugly so that your foot is held

securely. If the shoes feel as if they're pinching you, or your toes slide around when you are on the move, then they are not the right size.

Get measured

Although you may already know your shoe size, it's worth double-checking and being measured if you can, especially if you're a half-size or if one foot is bigger than the other. Many shoe stores don't offer this service any more, so it's a benefit to find somewhere that does. Some runners report that after years of running their shoe size goes up, due to their arches collapsing, so even long-term runners should have their feet measured occasionally.

A good, supportive pair of running shoes will be an expensive purchase, but you can look out for sale bargains. Remember that running is a relatively inexpensive sport and you don't need umpteen pieces of equipment, so this will be your most important investment.

tip *When you choose shoes, the key criteria should be fit, shock absorption, and stability. It's easy to be swayed by cheap prices, fancy claims, nice colors and convenient stores, but it's an important purchase, so take your time.*

MOTION-CONTROL

STABILITY

General running shoes

Shoes fall into one of three categories: stability, motion-control, or cushioned. The best type for you depends on the shape of your feet and how much stability you need.

CUSHIONED

To get an idea of your foot shape and running shoe needs, you can carry out the "Wet Footprint Test." When you get out of the shower or bath, place your wet feet onto a piece of cardboard and look at the imprint you leave. Armed with this knowledge, you'll be able to make a much more informed choice when shoe shopping, because the store assistant will be able to show you running shoes in the category that's right for you.

Flat feet

If you are flat-footed, your footprint will show the entire sole of your foot. You're likely to be an overpronator, which means that your foot lands on the outer side of your heel then rolls inward (pronates) too much, before you push off again from the ball of your foot and your toes. This running action can lead to a number of injuries. If you've got flat feet, then motion-control shoes are your best choice.

Motion-control shoes are cleverly designed to reduce the inward rolling action of the foot and ankle. They tend to be slightly heavier than other shoes, but they're durable, have good stability, and give great support to your feet.

Normal feet

If you have "normal" feet, your footprint will show the forefoot and heel connected by a broad band. You're likely to be a normal pronator, which means that when you run you land on the outside of your heel, roll slightly inward, and then push off again on the ball of your foot and your toes. This action means that your feet are already adept at shock absorption, so the best type of running shoe for you is a stability shoe.

Stability shoes are designed to prevent your foot from rolling too far inward, which could cause injury. Stability shoes also offer a good amount of cushioning and support for your feet.

OTHER TYPES OF RUNNING SHOE

Performance training shoes are lighter, tend to have less cushioning, and are designed for runners who do high-paced training. They are not suitable for beginners but may be a useful second pair as you become more advanced.

Racing shoes are extremely lightweight and have hardly any stability or cushioning. This type of shoe is aimed at elite runners who run fast races. This is definitely not a shoe for beginners.

Off-road, or trail, shoes are often reinforced to provide extra durability. They also have toe bumpers and increased traction on the soles and tend to be less cushioned than other types of shoes. Because they're designed for off-road, or trail, running, they may be a useful second pair if you're planning to do this type of running, but they shouldn't be used in place of a stability, motion-control, or cushioned shoe for general running.

RACING

OFF-ROAD

High-arched feet

If you have high-arched feet, your footprint will show a narrow band, or none at all, between the front of the foot and the heel. You're a supinator, which means that your foot lands on the outside of your heel but doesn't roll in enough before you push off again. Because of this, your feet won't be good shock absorbers. The most appropriate shoes are cushioned running shoes.

Cushioned shoes have softer midsoles and less stability than other running shoes, but they're designed to encourage foot motion, so they are ideal for those with high-arched feet.

***tip** If you're at the beach, this is the ideal place to study your footprints in the sand to find out what kind of feet you have.*

FLAT ARCH

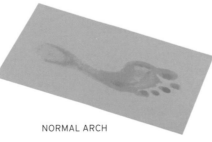

NORMAL ARCH

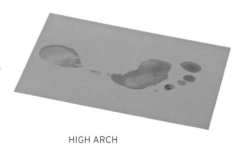

HIGH ARCH

Clothing and other equipment

Once you have yourself a good pair of running shoes, you should consider what clothing you'll wear when running, and if you need to invest in any other pieces of equipment.

When you're running you'll naturally become warm, so you don't want clothing that will cause you to overheat. It's best to wear layers because this will help keep you warm and dry, but still allow for ease of movement. If you get too hot, it's easy to remove a top layer and tie it around your waist. Although cotton fabrics are good at soaking up sweat, this doesn't make them ideal for wearing for long runs. Water and moisture is held by the fabric, so you end up wearing wet clothing. A wet T-shirt will stick to your body, chafing the skin and generally making you feel uncomfortable.

To avoid this problem, look for clothing made of breathable synthetic fabrics that have a wicking ability. This means that the material has the ability to transport moisture away from the body. Any moisture collects on the outside of the material and then evaporates, instead of being absorbed. The material won't stop you sweating, but it will prevent you from feeling damp and wet. Materials such as polyester/cotton and nylon/lycra have wicking ability, as well as specially made performance fabrics.

Use your own judgement as to how many layers to wear, and experiment with pants and shorts. During warm weather, a hat or cap will protect your head and sunglasses will shield your eyes. When it's colder, try a woollen hat, a small scarf, gloves, and an extra jacket for additional warmth.

LIGHT-REFLECTING ROAD GEAR

Socks

There is a whole array of running socks out there for you to choose from. The most important thing is that your socks fit your feet properly and are comfortable.

Thick cotton socks are soft and cosy, but they're not ideal if your feet are prone to sweating or if you will be running in wet weather. This is because cotton absorbs water, which can lead to the formation of blisters.

An alternative to cotton are socks made with a synthetic fiber that has wicking ability. Look for socks made of polyester/cotton and nylon/lycra, or special performance socks.

If you're going to be taking part in long runs or marathons, you may need to invest in some double-layer socks. As the name suggests, these socks consist of two layers of material and are useful in the prevention of blisters.

DOUBLE-LAYER SOCKS

STOPWATCH

Stopwatch

There is plenty of sophisticated equipment available, but the only thing you're likely to need when starting out is a stopwatch to keep track of your running times. A watch with a timer function would serve just as well, but if you'd rather buy a stopwatch for the purpose, don't be afraid to go for a basic option. High-tech versions can be useful and you can upgrade at a later stage, but they're unnecessary when you're starting out.

tip If you're running on roads, wear bright or light-reflecting clothes and shoes so that the traffic can see you at all times.

Sports bras

Women who run usually wear a sports bra. These are specially designed bras that provide extra support and comfort when you're moving around. You can choose between light or firm support.

Light support bras are designed to flatten the breasts against the body, so that they won't bounce around and cause discomfort. They're normally sold in sizes small, medium, and large, instead of in cup sizes, and are best for women who normally wear a size B cup or smaller. Firm support bras are usually sold by cup size and are designed with molded cups, so the breasts are firmly supported. They're recommended for women who wear a C cup or larger.

BREATHABLE SYNTHETIC FABRICS

YOUR FIRST RUN

You've bought the gear, you're psyched up, and now you want to run. Unfortunately, just going out and running as far as you can isn't always sensible, especially if you're new to exercise. The unaccustomed muscle use can be a shock to the system and it's easy to exhaust yourself or end up with strains and pains. If you don't want to be put off running before you've even begun, it's advisable to take things at a slower pace at the beginning.

So, take it slowly and build your strength and stamina gradually. To begin with, it's a good idea to take some brisk walks of 1–2 miles (2–3 km) distance. This will help activate all the key muscles used in running and stimulate your respiratory system.

Once you've done this, you can embark on a more structured program that incorporates short bursts of running and walking. It's up to you whether you choose to do this outdoors right away or to start off on a treadmill at the health club. The treadmill offers several benefits, especially the fact that it has a set pace and you won't find yourself suddenly having to go up or down a hill. Plus, it is a flat surface and won't cause undue stress on your body as you run.

If you are going to run outdoors, choose where you'll run carefully. Not all surfaces are ideal for your first attempts, or for running in general, and the shock impact of running on hard surfaces can cause strain and trauma to the body. The hardest surface is concrete and should be avoided. Grass can be fine to run on, as long as it's flat, even, and cut short. If it's too soft, it will place undue strain on your body, and if it's too long it will be difficult to run on. Tarmac is preferable to concrete, especially during the summer months, and is okay if you have no other options.

The run-walk program

The run-walk program is designed to acclimatize your body slowly to running, instead of shocking it with a full-blown running regime. It incorporates bursts of running with walking and by the end of it you should be able to run for 20 minutes nonstop, without needing to take breaks.

Ideally, you should complete three sessions of the program every week, before progressing to the next week. Each week builds up the amount of running you do, so you can quickly and easily assess your progress. Before each session, make sure you do a brief warm-up exercise first and, at the end, a cool down is recommended. For this program, walking for 5–10 minutes beforehand and walking for 5 minutes afterward should be sufficient, but once you're running for 20 minutes or more, you can switch to the warm-up and cool-down routines recommended in this book.

Make sure you have either a stopwatch or a timer on your watch to ensure you keep track of your running and walking times.

WEEK ONE

In your first week, aim to complete the following routine a total of three times:

Run for 1 minute, then walk for 2 minutes.
Run for 1 minute, then walk for 2 minutes.
Run for 2 minutes, then walk for 2 minutes.
Run for 2 minutes, then walk for 2 minutes.
Run for 1 minute, then walk for 2 minutes.
Run for 1 minute, then walk for 2 minutes.

It may not feel like you're doing much running, but when you've completed this first session once, you'll have run for a total of 8 minutes. If you repeat it three times in a week that's 24 minutes—congratulations!

WEEK TWO

This builds on the effort you've put in during the first week. It adds 2 minutes to the total running time and includes one burst of running for 3 minutes.

Run for 1 minute, then walk for 2 minutes.
Run for 1 minute, then walk for 2 minutes.
Run for 2 minutes, then walk for 2 minutes.
Run for 3 minutes, then walk for 2 minutes.
Run for 2 minutes, then walk for 2 minutes.
Run for 1 minute, then walk for 2 minutes.

This takes your total running time per session to 10 minutes. If you complete this three times during the week, you're now running for 30 minutes a week.

WEEK THREE

This week incorporates another 3-minute run, taking your total running time per session up to 12 minutes.

Run for 1 minute, walk for 2 minutes.
Run for 2 minutes, walk for 2 minutes.
Run for 3 minutes, walk for 3 minutes.
Run for 3 minutes, walk for 2 minutes.
Run for 2 minutes, walk for 2 minutes.
Run for 1 minute, walk for 2 minutes.

If you complete three sessions this week, you'll be up to 36 minutes of running, over half an hour in total.

tip If you're running on roads, remember to wear bright or light-reflecting clothes and shoes so that traffic in both directions can see you at all times. Always carry a cell phone and, if you could be out of signal range, loose change for a pay phone.

WEEK FOUR

In this week there will be a reduction in the number of minutes walking and an increase in the time running.

Run for 2 minutes, walk for 1½ minutes.
Run for 5 minutes, walk for 1½ minutes.
Run for 5 minutes, walk for 1½ minutes.
Run for 3 minutes, walk for 1½ minutes.

In each session, you'll now be running for 15 minutes.

WEEK FIVE

This week sees another reduction in the time you spend walking, increasing one burst of running to 8 minutes.

Run for 2 minutes, walk for 1 minute.
Run for 5 minutes, walk for 1 minute.
Run for 8 minutes, walk for 1 minute.
Run for 3 minutes, walk for 1 minute.

You'll be running for 18 minutes in each session—that's an impressive 54 minutes in a week.

WEEK SIX

In the sixth week, you'll increase the biggest burst of running by another 2 minutes and continue walking in between for 1 minute.

Run for 2 minutes, walk for 1 minute.
Run for 3 minutes, walk for 1 minute.
Run for 10 minutes, walk for 1 minute.
Run for 3 minutes, walk for 1 minute.

After each session, you'll again have run for 18 minutes, but will have increased the time that you can keep going.

WEEK SEVEN

This week you'll finally be running for 20 minutes in total, with a long 12-minute burst making up the bulk of it.

Run for 4 minutes, walk for 1 minute.
Run for 12 minutes, walk for 1 minute.
Run for 4 minutes, walk for 1 minute.

You're fast approaching being able to run for 20 minutes non-stop. As much as you may want to rush out and try 20 minutes in one go now, it's advisable to continue to build up your pace for a few more weeks.

WEEK EIGHT

Run for 3 minutes, walk for 1 minute.
Run for 14 minutes, walk for 1 minute.
Run for 3 minutes, walk for 1 minute.

WEEK NINE

Run for 2 minutes, walk for 1 minute.
Run for 16 minutes, walk for 1 minute.
Run for 2 minutes, walk for 1 minute.

WEEK TEN

This is the week that was a far-off dream when you started. If you've completed all of the above training, you should now be able to run for 20 minutes nonstop. Congratulations, you've made it!

2

Running Techniques

Like any exercise, running involves a range of techniques. If you're a beginner, these techniques won't necessarily come naturally, but with a bit of help, guidance, and practice they are easily learned. This section focuses on key issues for runners, from warming up properly and stretching muscles, to running posture and cross-training methods.

DEVELOPING YOUR RUNNING ABILITY

As with any skill, there is a variety of techniques and basic concepts you can learn that will develop your running ability and help you get the most out of it. Some abilities develop naturally and you can, to some extent, run for pleasure without worrying too much about technique. But if you want to gain the most from running, or perhaps progress to take part in organized runs or races, it is to your advantage to learn the basics and work on your techniques.

One important benefit of getting the techniques right is that it will ensure you are working with yourself, not against yourself. Those new to running often leap straight into it without taking the time to learn the key elements. Although you might appear to be running okay, closer inspection could reveal things you are doing that are actually hindering your progress. It might only be a detail, like positioning your arms incorrectly or leaning forward too much as you run, but even minor mistakes in technique have an effect. By getting your techniques correct, you can become more adept at running and potentially faster, too.

Stride length

The pace, or speed, of your running is influenced by the length of your strides and, therefore, the number of steps you take over a certain distance. New runners are often tempted to take longer strides, believing this will help them to run better, but this can be detrimental and lead to "overstriding." It might seem logical that to cover more ground you need to take bigger steps, but this is not always the case. The longer your stride, the more likely it is that you'll land heavily and awkwardly, and this significantly increases the risk of injury.

While increasing stride length is achievable by intermediate runners who will approach this by pushing with the rear leg, instead of reaching out with the front leg, for beginners it's easier to improve performance by increasing stride frequency—or cadence—instead.

Stride frequency

Cadence is largely an individual issue and your frequency will depend on your general running ability. Research suggests that the average stride frequency

of most runners is about 80-85 strides per minute and this is a good rate to aim for. At the highest level of the sport, Olympic-standard runners achieve an average of 180 strides per minute. You can count your stride frequency by counting how many steps you take per minute, or the number of times each foot strikes the ground. It may be difficult to do this yourself, but someone else can count for you, or you could film yourself in action, slow down the recording, and count your strides that way.

One simple technique for increasing your cadence is running quickly up a flight of stairs. This will train you to take smaller and quicker steps. At first, try running up the stairs quickly, then walking down; as you build up your ability you can run down the stairs, too. But don't try to do too much—practicing this technique once a week, for 5-10 minutes, should be sufficient.

Another method that can help to boost your cadence is to imagine you are running on a bed of hot coals and have to get across them without getting burned. Practice this over a short distance, of say 50 yds (45 m), once or twice a week.

Remember to remain relaxed. If you aren't relaxed and are holding tension in any area of your body, it's not possible to run well. Not only does it hinder your running ability, it also increases the risk of muscle pain and injury.

tip *Another useful method for increasing cadence is to use a pace beeper gadget. They're inexpensive and are worn around the neck or kept in a pocket. They work by emitting a beep—the beep is designed to help you keep pace as you run and the gadget can be set to beep at a certain stride rate, so you can use it to effectively emit beeps for your target cadence.*

TECHNIQUES

Stop and watch other runners jogging around the park or taking part in longer runs, and they make running look like one of the easiest forms of exercise there is. It's true: running is relatively easy once you get into it. However, an awareness of the techniques involved will ensure you start out on the right track and get the most you can out of running. Once you've got the hang of the techniques and integrated them into your running, they'll soon seem like second nature.

Arm positioning

If you've never run before, or at least not since you were a child, knowing what to do with your arms, or how they should be held when you are running, can be an issue. Mimicking the arm positions of other runners might feel unnatural, and it's important that you take the time to find a position that works for you. The aim is to allow your arms to swing comfortably and naturally by your body as you run.

The arms of a runner play almost as important a part as the legs, because they help to stabilize the body and propel it forward. If your arms are too rigid or too floppy, they'll affect overall movement. For example, if your arms are positioned too high up, they could affect your strides and make them shorter, as well as cause tension and muscle fatigue in your shoulders and upper back. But if your arms are positioned too low down, then they may cause a side-to-side bouncing motion as you move.

Ideally, your running arm position should be located between your waist and your chest. Your arms should swing naturally by your body as you move, with your elbows away from your body. Each runner's arm position will vary, so it doesn't matter if you hold your arms slightly higher or lower than other people. The important thing is to find a position that's right for you and that helps you move along easily.

Breathing

Knowing how to breathe properly while running is also a concern for many people. To some degree, feeling "puffed out" is natural when you're exercising, but breathing too quickly in certain situations, such as when running uphill, can cause hyperventilation. Some runners go by the rule that you should breathe in through the nose and out through the mouth, but sticking to this can be difficult if you're concentrating on your running.

One of the best ways to regulate your breathing when running is simply to breathe naturally. You don't need to learn tricky techniques or follow breathing mantras, just relax and breathe slowly. Don't make the mistake of

taking short, sharp breaths and of only breathing from your chest. By taking deep breaths from your stomach, your breathing will be easier to control and this will enhance your running performance.

Optimizing performance

It's also worth spending time working on your postural technique, or how you align your body while you run. This involves checking how your head, shoulders, torso, and hips are positioned while you run and how you can improve your running technique by making subtle changes.

As you progress and reach an intermediate level, issues, such as your foot strike—where and how your foot strikes the ground as you run—and the nature of your strides, are also likely to become important. Your foot strike can affect both your running performance and your risk of developing injuries, so there are many benefits to be gained from getting it right. Working on your strides can help you run faster, which is particularly useful if you plan to do any racing.

POSTURE AND BREATHING

Maintaining good posture will help your running technique and also reduces the risk of injury. The position of your arms affects your overall running ability and performance, so finding the perfect position has numerous benefits. You can find your optimum arm position by determining where your arms fall naturally when you move. If you can't find a comfortable arm position this way, don't panic! It doesn't work for everyone and you may prefer the standing-still approach.

Good breathing is also important. It's easy to take breathing for granted, but how you breathe while you're walking will—or should—differ from how you breathe when you're running. Take the time to work on your breathing technique and you'll reap the benefits as you run.

RUNNING BREATHING TECHNIQUE

1 Lie on your back on an exercise mat or a firm surface. Place one hand on your chest and the other hand on your lower stomach (*far right*).

2 Breathe in as you normally do and see which hand moves the most. Is it the one on your chest or your stomach?

3 If the answer is the hand on your chest, you are breathing shallowly and need to make the hand on your stomach move more. It should rise as you inhale and fall as you exhale.

4 Take another deep breath in, this time breathing right down to your stomach. This will allow more oxygen into your lungs and help relax your whole body.

tip *Learning to breathe from your stomach instead of your chest can take time, especially when you've been used to shallow breathing for a long time. Practice the method when you can, then gradually apply it as you run. Don't worry if it doesn't come naturally at first; the more you practice, the more you'll adjust to it.*

FINDING YOUR RUNNING ARM POSITION—WHILE MOVING

1 To find your natural running arm position, start running slowly with your arms dangling down by your sides.

2 Relax and don't think about what your arms are doing or where they should be. Keep looking straight ahead.

3 Slowly move your arms up to a comfortable position (*left*). Don't think too much about what you're doing with them, but let them find their place in the natural rhythm of your running body.

FINDING YOUR RUNNING ARM POSITION—WHILE STANDING STILL

1 Stand up straight with your legs hip-distance apart and your back straight.

2 Hold out your arms in front of you, with the palms of your hands facing down. Keep your mind calm and try not to think too much about what you're about to do.

3 Slowly relax, bend your elbows, and let your arms drop to your sides, still with elbows bent (*right*).

4 The position in which your arms have now come to rest should be the natural running position for your arms.

5 Jog on the spot or run for a few minutes and see how this position feels to you.

IDEAL RUNNING POSITION

1 To discover your ideal running position, keep your back straight, your hips forward, and buttocks tucked in.

2 Your head should be held high, with your face and jaw relaxed. Keep your eyes focused straight ahead, so you can see exactly where you're running and any obstacles that may be in your path.

3 Check your shoulders are relaxed, not hunched, and that your hands are hanging loosely.

tip *Don't obsess about your running posture or worry that your posture is different from other people's. Everyone has a slightly different posture and, as long as you're not doing anything that could induce injury, it's better to stick with your own style if it works for you.*

COMMON POSTURE MISTAKES

The following postural mistakes are common in runners, and can have detrimental results:

LEANING TOO FAR FORWARD

This places an extra burden on the leg muscles and can lead to problems with the shins, Achilles tendonitis, or back pain. It also affects the length of your stride, because it can force your hips back farther.

The only instance when leaning forward slightly is recommended is when running uphill. This is because leaning into the angle of the hill will help you maintain your center of gravity and better equip you to tackle the run. Other techniques should also be employed when hill running, and arm action is important in keeping you propelled upward.

LEANING TOO FAR BACKWARD

This adversely affects both the legs and back, and prevents the runner from breathing deeply from the stomach. It also acts as a kind of braking device, slowing down your running pace.

TILTING YOUR CHIN

Tilting the chin upward, so that it points toward the sky, is a mistake often made near the end of a run, when the runner is fatigued. Try to keep your neck and chin at right angles to avoid straining your neck.

HUNCHING YOUR SHOULDERS

Some runners hunch their shoulders or draw their shoulder blades together. As well as making running awkward, this can cause unnecessary tension in the shoulders. If you want to run efficiently, your body needs to be relaxed.

HOLDING YOUR HEAD TOO FAR FORWARD OR BACKWARD

Neither position will help your running, and both cause unnecessary strain and tension in the neck. To keep your head straight, imagine you are balancing something on top of it, that you don't want to drop.

LEANING TOO FAR FORWARD

TILTING YOUR CHIN

Striking and striding

To develop your running technique, you need to know how best to position your feet, take strides, and how far to stride. Many of these elements come naturally, but considering the theory behind the practice can lead to noticeable improvements in your performance.

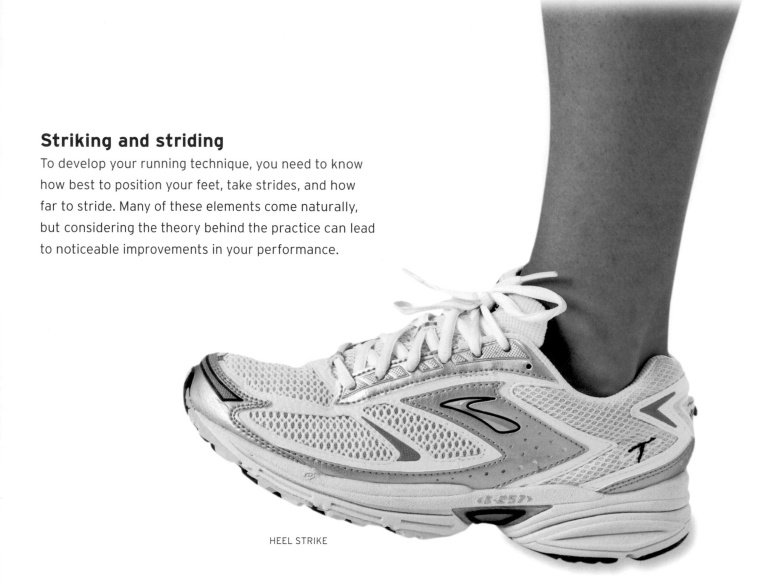

HEEL STRIKE

FOOT POSITION

Your running feet should point straight ahead. Try to avoid turning either or both of your feet inward or outward and ensure you're standing flat on the ground, without arching. Run in a straight line and make sure your feet don't cross over each other, because this will hinder your progress. Unless you have problems with your feet, this advice should be easy to follow and will give you a good starting point for running.

FOOT STRIKE

Foot strike literally means the way your foot strikes the ground when you run. There are two main types of foot strike—heel strike and toe strike. It doesn't matter which type of foot striker you are, because it's a case of going with whatever feels natural, but bear in mind that it could be a factor in your posture. If you're not sure what type of foot strike you have, get a friend to watch you in action.

HEEL STRIKERS

Heel strikers land heel first. They roll through their feet, then push off the ground again with their toes. Their posture is upright, so the center of gravity is directly above where their heel lands. More runners are heel strikers than toe strikers.

tip If you're a heel striker, look out for sneakers with reinforced heels, because they will last longer.

OVERSTRIDING

Overstriding is where a runner attempts unnaturally long strides. This is not good practice because it can interfere with your natural running stride. You can tell if you're guilty of this from the way you reach with your lead leg. If this leg is straight as it reaches the ground, you are overstriding.

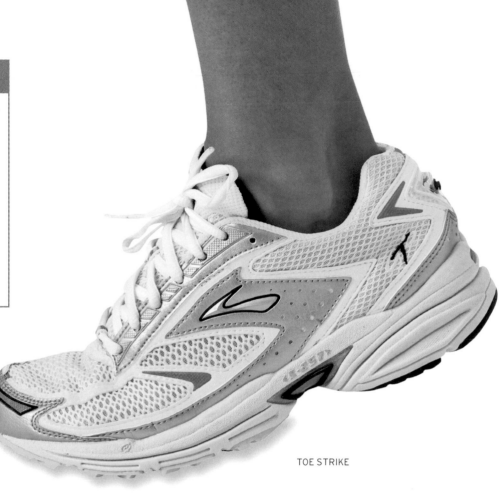

TOE STRIKE

TOE STRIKERS

Toe strikers land on the ball of their feet, near their toes. They roll back onto their heels and then push off the ground again with their heels. Toe strikers tend to lean forward slightly, so their center of gravity is above where their foot lands on the ground.

tip If you are a toe striker, your shoes may wear out quicker in the toe area. You may benefit from orthotics, or special insoles in your running shoes, to help cushion your feet and provide extra support.

STRIDE LENGTH

Beginners often worry about their stride length and whether or not their strides are long enough. On the whole, when you're new to running, the length of your stride shouldn't be a major concern. Although longer strides do help you to run faster and cover more ground, overstriding can hinder your progress and increase the risk of injury. Instead, try to find your natural stride position, in which you're not forcing the length of your strides and are running in a relaxed and comfortable manner.

tip Once you are more accustomed to running, you can work on gently increasing your stride length, as well as your turnover.

WARMING UP

As keen as you might be to rush out of the door and get running, it's important to take the time to warm up properly first. Warming up is one of the most crucial elements of any exercise program and a habit that should precede each and every run, whether you're just starting out or you have been running for years. Don't be tempted to skip it, or you could end up paying for it later. Run without warming up first and your muscles will be cold, stiff, and tense, making you susceptible to injuries and soreness.

Warming up also means you get the best out of running, from both a performance and enjoyment point of view. It increases the blood flow around your body and warms up your muscles, helping them become more flexible and supple, while adjusting your body gradually to the exercise it will be receiving. With this groundwork in place, the running itself will seem easier.

TAKE IT EASY

A warm-up is not the time to push yourself hard, but rather to get your body gently moving. The emphasis should be on waking your body up slowly, so choose the pace that feels right to you. Don't feel pressured to compete with any running companions. Stick to a slow and comfortable pace, and you'll gain just as much. It's not speed that counts in a warm-up, but the effort you put in. As a rough guide, you shouldn't feel breathless or unable to talk as you jog during a warm-up—if you are, slow down and adopt an easier pace.

Effective warm-ups

An ideal warm-up consists of a 5-10 minute slow jog or brisk walk. Some people like to jog on the spot for 5 minutes and then jog around for another 5 minutes. The combination you choose is up to you, and you can vary it from session to session if you want. If you have a history of circulation problems and you're going out on a cold morning, it is a good idea to have a warm shower beforehand. This will help begin to ease stiff muscles and put you in a better position for your warm-up.

You know you've warmed up if you can feel your body temperature rise. You shouldn't find yourself boiling hot at this point (if you are, then you've probably worked yourself too hard), but you may find yourself wanting to undo the zipper of your jacket or remove an outer layer of clothing. More oxygen and blood are brought to your muscles, your heart will be beating a little faster, you may be breathing a little more heavily, and your overall circulation will have improved.

These elements are all good signs. It means there will be less stress on your heart when you begin running properly and it will be less of a shock to the system to make the adjustment between gentle and more vigorous exercise, because your cardiovascular system will be prepared. Plus, your muscles will have limbered up and you'll be less likely to strain them.

Even when you've warmed up your body and your muscles, it's still not time to launch into your run. The next stage is to perform a few stretching exercises to loosen up individual muscles even further. After that, you'll be well prepared to start running.

STRETCHING

The question of whether or not you should stretch before exercise has been the subject of some debate over the years. The current general consensus is that it's a good idea to stretch the muscles and put them through a full range of movements before you run, but that this should follow a short pre-run warm-up jog of about 5-10 minutes. The warm-up gets the blood flowing and puts you in a better position to start stretching, because warm muscles will stretch more easily.

Stopping to perform stretching exercises may seem pointless when all you want to do is get on with running, but it's worth taking the time to do so. You may not achieve any immediate or obvious results, but doing regular stretching exercises and looking after your muscles will pay off in the long term. Not only will it help reduce the risk of injury, but it could help reduce sore muscles after running and improve your overall performance, too. In addition, stretching can provide relief for stiff joints, improve your circulation, enhance your muscle tone, and improve your balance.

Effective stretching

Stretching exercises can be performed indoors or outdoors. If you're outside, you'll need to find yourself a suitable and sturdy prop for performing some of the stretches—a wall, tree or even a lamp-post should be fine. Be aware that the surface you stand on may affect your stretching ability. Ideally, you need a firm surface, but a sidewalk or bare floor might be too hard and prevent you from relaxing and stretching properly, whereas firm grass is perfect. If you're indoors, a thick carpet is ideal, or consider investing in an exercise mat.

When you're performing stretching exercises, try to move slowly and don't try to force a stretch. Stretching slowly and gently will relax and lengthen the muscles, while jerking movements may make muscles contract and cause tension. Never try to bounce either, because this increases the risk of pulling or tearing a muscle.

Aim to hold the stretch in each position for about 10-15 seconds, or as long as it feels comfortable. Feeling mild tension in the muscles is normal and a good sign that you're working the muscle, but avoid overstretching.

It can be tempting to push yourself harder, especially if you're trying to keep up with someone else who seems more flexible than you or you want to see how far you can push yourself, but it's much better for your body to understretch than overstretch.

At first, aim to perform each stretching exercise twice on each leg or body part. As you progress and become more flexible, you can increase the number of times you repeat each individual exercise in each warm-up session. The important thing to remember is not to overdo it or attempt more than your body can cope with. Your fitness level and muscle ability cannot be rushed, but if you stick with it and do all you can to improve it, results will become visible in time.

An ideal set of stretching exercises focuses on several crucial areas of the lower body, including the upper and lower calves, the back of the thighs (hamstrings), and the front of the thighs (quadriceps). In addition, you may want to do a few extra stretches to help release tension in your upper body. The chest, shoulder, back, bicep, and tricep stretches are ideal for this.

CAUTION!

If you experience sudden pain anywhere in your body, stop and rest. If a muscle is sore or injured, don't attempt to stretch it because this could aggravate the problem. Follow any medical advice you've been given, and wait until the soreness or injury has healed before continuing with your usual stretching routine.

LEG STRETCHES

These stretching exercises focus on the upper and lower calf muscles, the front of the thigh (quadriceps), and the back of the thigh (hamstring). These muscles are all susceptible to injury when running, but stretching can reduce this risk.

LOWER CALF STRETCH

1 Stand facing a wall or tree with your left leg bent slightly and your right leg behind you.

2 Bring your right leg in a bit further and bend it, lowering your hips slightly as you do so. Keep the heel of your right foot on the floor (*right*).

3 Hold for 10-15 seconds, then relax. Repeat the stretch a second time. You might not feel this stretch as much as the upper calf stretch (*see below*).

4 Change legs to stretch the lower calf muscle on your left leg. Repeat the stretch twice.

UPPER CALF STRETCH

1 Stand facing a wall or tree, with your right leg bent slightly and your left leg extended straight out behind you. Place your hands flat against the wall or tree.

2 Keep both your heels flat on the floor and both your feet facing forward.

3 Keep your back straight and lean forward a little (*right*). You should feel the stretch in your upper-right calf.

4 Hold position for 10-15 seconds, then relax. Repeat the stretch a second time.

5 Change position so your right leg is extended out behind you and you can stretch your right calf muscle. Again, repeat the stretch twice.

FRONT OF THIGH OR QUADRICEPS STRETCH

1 Stand sideways next to a wall or tree and place your left hand flat on it. Ensure your left leg is slightly bent and keep both knees close together.

2 Bend your right leg back and take hold of your right foot with your right hand. Slowly bring your leg in as far as you can to your backside (*above*). You should be able to feel the stretch in the front of your right thigh.

3 Hold the stretch for 10-15 seconds, then relax. Repeat the stretch a second time with the same leg, then change and stretch the left leg.

tip *This stretch can be increased by clenching your buttocks together while holding your foot up to your backside in step 2.*

BACK OF THIGH OR HAMSTRING STRETCH

1 Stand in front of a low step. Straighten your left leg and put your left heel on the step; your right leg should be slightly bent. Rest your hands on your left thigh.

2 Gently bend forward from the hip (*above*). Keep your back straight and stick your buttocks out, so you can feel the stretch down the back of your left thigh.

3 Keep your right leg slightly bent throughout the stretch and try not to round your shoulders. Hold the position for 10-15 seconds, then relax. Repeat a second time before swapping over to stretch the other hamstring.

tip *The hamstring muscles play an important role in running by providing the pushing action that enables us to run.*

UPPER-BODY STRETCHES

An ideal stretching routine focuses on the whole body, not just your legs. These exercises concentrate on key areas of your upper body, including the chest, shoulders, back, and arms.

CROSS-SHOULDER STRETCH

1 Stand up straight with your knees relaxed, your feet hip-distance apart and toes pointing forward.

2 Bend your right arm and extend it across your chest.

3 Place your left hand on your right upper arm or the right elbow so that you are supporting your arm (right).

4 Slowly ease your right arm in toward you. As you do so, you should feel the stretch across the back of your right shoulder and arm.

5 Hold for 10-15 seconds, then relax. Repeat a second time, then stretch your left shoulder in the same way.

tip *This stretch can also be performed from a sitting position. If sitting, ensure your back is straight at all times and your feet are placed firmly on the ground.*

TRICEP STRETCH

1 Stand up straight with your knees relaxed, your feet hip-distance apart and toes pointing forward.

2 Bend your right arm and lift it so it's next to your head. The fingers on your right hand should touch your shoulder blades.

3 Place your left arm across your head and your left hand on your right elbow (below). You should feel a stretch in your right tricep.

4 Hold for 10-15 seconds, then relax. Repeat, then change arms and stretch your left tricep.

UPPER-BACK STRETCH

1 Stand up straight with your knees relaxed, your feet hip-distance apart and toes pointing forward.

2 Link your hands together in front of your chest, with your palms facing away from your body.

3 Push your hands away from your chest to form a right angle between your body and your arms (*right*). As you do so, you should feel a stretch in your upper back.

4 Breathe slowly and hold for 10-15 seconds, then relax. Repeat the stretch a second time.

BICEP STRETCH

1 Stand up straight with your knees relaxed, your feet hip-distance apart and toes pointing forward.

2 Lift your arms up to shoulder height, so they form a right angle with your body (*above*).

3 Slowly rotate your wrists, so your palms face behind you. You should be able to feel the stretch in your biceps, or upper arms.

4 Hold for 10-15 seconds, then relax. Repeat a second time.

CHEST STRETCH

1 Stand up straight with your knees relaxed, your feet hip-distance apart and your toes pointing forward.

2 Put your arms behind your lower back and clasp your hands together.

3 Slowly pull your shoulder blades back toward each other and, at the same time, raise your arms slightly to open up your chest (*left*).

4 Hold this position for 10-15 seconds, then relax. Repeat the exercise.

COOLING DOWN

Just as your body needs to be warmed up properly before running, it needs to cool down again afterward. A sprint finish followed by sudden collapse and no movement for hours won't do your body any good. Stopping suddenly after vigorous exercise can cause all kinds of unwanted side effects, such as muscle cramps, dizziness and general soreness. So, as tempting as it is, it's best to avoid sitting down immediately after running. You should also avoid having a warm shower or a sauna until you've cooled down properly.

Cooling down enables your body to return gently to its pre-exercise state. It helps your heart rate and breathing to slow down and lessens the chances of your muscles becoming sore and stiff. It also prevents your blood from pooling in the legs, which can occur after a hard run. Plus, it's an opportunity for you to begin to relax after what may have been a period of intense activity.

CAUTION!

The stretches should all be relatively easy to do and your muscles should feel flexible. If for any reason you feel pain in your muscles, or they're unexpectedly sore or stiff, don't push the stretches. It's better to relax instead of trying to force it, because at the end of your cool-down routine you should be left feeling relaxed and energized, not tense and sore.

Effective cooling down

Ideally, you should aim to ease gently into the cool-down period. As your running session comes to an end, slow down into a gentle jog for the last 5 minutes. This will help your heart rate and breathing begin to return to normal. After 5 minutes of jogging, slow down to a walking pace. Try to keep moving for a few more minutes, especially if your breathing isn't quite back to its pre-exercise state. If you've had a particularly hard run or have taken part in a race, you may need to extend your final jog to about 10 minutes so that your body can adjust sufficiently.

As in the warm-up routine, stretching exercises play an important part in cooling down, too. Once you're satisfied that you're relaxed and breathing normally, it's time to get stretching. Your cool-down stretching session should last about 10–15 minutes. In contrast to your warm-up stretches, because your muscles will already be very warm and in a flexible state, it's possible to include some more advanced stretches. Ideally, you should try to stretch all the major muscle groups, focusing particularly on the muscles you've used during your run. You can incorporate some of the exercises from your warm-up, as well as additional ones.

Many of the cool-down stretches involve the need to be sitting or lying on the ground, so you may want to use an exercise mat. The likelihood is that the end of your run will coincide with returning home, where it's easy to carry out floor exercises. If you're out and about, look for a suitable patch of grass to use for your final stretching routine—it may help, for example, to plan where you'll do them before you start running so you know where you're heading for at the end. Having a final destination also helps keep you focused and gives you something to aim for.

tip *If you've been running with friends or a group, the cool-down period provides an ideal social ending to your exercise session. It's a chance to catch up with others and see how they fared during the course of the run, talk about the route you've just covered, share tips and advice, or finish conversations that you started mid-run. Even if you've run on your own, it's a chance to take stock of your thoughts and wind down slowly.*

COOLING DOWN-LEGS

The following exercises concentrate on the major leg muscles used during your run, including the calves, hamstrings, hips, and thighs. There's also a buttocks stretch as these muscles are closely connected to the leg, and this stretch will benefit your outer thigh.

INNER THIGH STRETCH

1 Stand up straight with your legs wide apart and your feet facing forward.

2 Bend your left knee while keeping your right leg straight out to the side (*above*). You should feel a stretch going down the inside of your right thigh.

3 Hold for 10-15 seconds, then relax. Repeat, then stretch the inner thigh of your left leg in the same way.

GLUTEAL, OR BUTTOCKS, STRETCH

1 Lie on your back with your knees bent.

2 Take your left leg and move it across your right leg, so your left ankle lies just above your right knee and your left knee is pointing out to the side.

3 Gently use your hands to move your right leg toward you. It should carry your left leg with it (*above*). You should feel the stretch in your buttocks and the outer thigh of your left leg.

4 Hold the position for 10-15 seconds, then relax. Repeat, then stretch the right leg in the same way.

FRONT OF HIP STRETCH

1 Kneel down with your left knee on the floor and your right knee bent at a right angle in front of you.

2 Keep your right foot flat on the floor and pointing forward. Slowly lean forward. Rest your hands on your right leg.

3 You should be able to feel the stretch in the front of your left hip.

4 Hold for 10-15 seconds, then relax. Repeat, then stretch your right hip in the same way.

HAMSTRING AND CALF STRETCH

1 Sit on the floor with your legs stretched out in front of you.

2 Slowly bend your upper body forward, taking care to keep your back straight. You should be able to feel the stretch in the back of your thighs, or hamstrings.

3 Reach your hands forward and touch the tops of your toes, allowing your knees to bend slightly if you need to (*above right*). At this point you should be able to feel the stretch in both your hamstrings and the back of your calves.

4 Hold for 10-15 seconds, then relax. Repeat a second time.

OUTER THIGH, OR ILLIOTIBIAL, STRETCH

1 Kneel down with your left knee on the floor and your right knee bent at a right angle in front of you.

2 Keep your right foot flat on the floor and pointing forward. Slowly lean forward, resting your hands on your right knee. At the same time, move your left hip slightly out to the side (*below*). You should feel the stretch at the side of your left hip and down the outside of your left thigh.

3 Hold the position for 10-15 seconds, then relax. Repeat, then stretch the right leg in the same way.

tip The illiotibial band is a tough band of connective tissue that runs the length of your outer thigh.

COOLING DOWN—UPPER BODY

It's not only your legs that need stretching. The following exercises gently stretch your upper body, arms, backs and groin. They will help loosen the muscles, reduce tension, and aid relaxation.

LYING QUADRICEPS STRETCH

1 Lie down on your left side and place one leg on top of the other. Ensure you are balanced by propping yourself up—put your left arm, from the elbow to the hand, flat on the ground and your right hand flat on the floor in front of you.

2 Slowly bring your left leg up behind you and grab hold of your foot with your right hand.

3 Slowly pull your foot close to your body, while pushing your right hip slightly forward (*below*). You should feel the stretch in the quadriceps in the front of your right thigh.

4 Hold for 10 seconds, then relax. Repeat, then switch sides and stretch the left thigh in the same way.

GROIN STRETCH

1 Sit on the floor with your back straight.

2 Bend your legs and bring them toward your body. Bring your feet together, so the soles of your feet are touching each other.

3 Hold your feet and position your arms so your elbows are on the inside of your knees (*above*). Slowly lean forward, while gently pressing your knees toward the ground.

4 You should be able to feel this stretch in your groin. Hold for 10-15 seconds, then relax. Repeat a second time.

tip *The closer your feet are to your body, the more intense the stretch will be. As you become more adept, you can use your leg muscles to press your knees downward.*

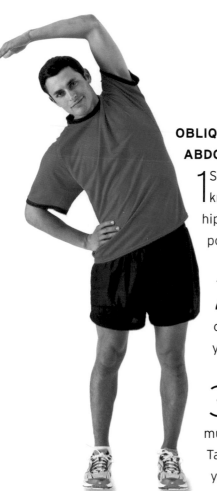

OBLIQUE OR SIDE ABDOMINAL STRETCH

1 Stand up straight with your knees relaxed, your feet hip-distance apart and toes pointing forward.

2 Put one hand on your waist and bring the other hand over the top of your head.

3 Lean gently sideways until you feel your side muscles stretching (*left*). Take care you don't twist your body.

4 Hold for 10-15 seconds, then relax. Repeat a second time, then stretch the other side.

tip This exercise helps improve the oblique muscles, which support the lower back. It also helps your posture and reduces the risk of back pain.

UPPER-BODY STRETCH

1 Stand up straight with your knees relaxed, your feet hip-distance apart and toes pointing forward.

2 Raise your arms above your head and clasp your hands together. Straighten your arms and stretch them upward, while continuing to look forward (*right*). You should feel the stretch in your arms, chest, upper back, and shoulders.

3 Hold for 10-15 seconds, then relax. Repeat a second time.

BACK STRETCH

1 Lie on your back. Bend your knees up toward your chest, so your legs are at a right angle.

2 Put your hands behind your knees and slowly pull the backs of your thighs toward your chest (*left*). Ensure your lower back is flat on the floor or mat.

3 Hold for 10-15 seconds, then relax. Repeat a second time.

CROSS TRAINING

If you're running with the aim of improving your fitness, or want to take part in charity fun runs or races, you may want to incorporate cross training into your weekly routine. Cross training means combining two or more sports, or forms of exercise, with the aim of improving your overall fitness levels.

Many runners also train in another sport, and there are benefits to doing this regardless of ability–whether you're just starting out, have been running for a while, or are involved in extensive training. The sooner you start, the better. Depending on what additional activities you do, you'll be less likely to be hampered by aching legs or have shortness of breath, and the more you train the more your fitness levels will improve.

If, on the other hand, you stick solely to running, the repetitive action and continued use of the same muscles are bound to place a degree of unwanted stress on certain muscles and parts of your body. By incorporating other forms of exercise into your schedule, you'll be using different muscles and the stress on these other areas will be reduced. It will also give you the chance to exercise a wider range of muscles. This will have a positive effect on your overall fitness, improving your strength and flexibility, and being fitter will have a beneficial knock-on effect on your running.

Cross training also allows you to inject some variety into your fitness regime, so you're not doing the same routine week in, week out. Running all the time can become boring. If you give yourself other sporting activities to focus on, you may end up improving your motivation as a runner.

Cross-training options

There's a wide selection of alternative sports and exercises that can count as cross training. Popular choices include gym work, core stability training, swimming, and cycling, because these are all proven to be beneficial to runners. Other activities are aerobics, kick boxing, rowing, skiing, and skating. It's up to you what additional activities you'd like to take part in, and

USING CROSS TRAINING TO IMPROVE WEAKNESSES

If there's a particular part of your body that you know is weaker or could benefit from additional training, plan your cross training with this in mind. Some types of exercise will benefit you personally more than others. As a rough guide:

To strengthen the quadriceps, consider cycling, rowing, swimming, skating, or skiing.

For the upper body, consider swimming, walking, rowing, or skiing.

For the abdominals, choose skiing, rowing, or running in water (aqua jogging).

For the ankles, consider swimming or running in water (aqua jogging).

For the lower back, try swimming or rowing.

For the hips, try cycling or skiing.

you can make your cross-training program as structured or as flexible as you wish.

If you're just starting out and are not sure what would be best for you, try cycling or swimming, because these are a good all-round starting basis for cross training. Like running, cycling involves the use of the leg muscles, but places less stress on the body. This means you can usually cycle for longer without feeling discomfort. Swimming is another good cardiovascular activity and has the added benefit that you can do it even if your legs are tired from running (this is what's known as "active recovery"), because the water will help ease stiffness. Swimming and cycling are also useful skills to keep going should you aspire to racing, because you may want to take part in a triathlon and these particular sports are the other components.

tip *Beginners should try to balance out their running with cross training. If you're running twice a week, do two cross-training sessions.*

Core stability

Core stability refers to the training of the abdominal muscles to support and stabilize the spine. It's a discipline widely used by sportspeople, not least runners, as well as anyone wanting to improve their fitness, muscles, and posture. It's also a concept drawn on in Pilates and yoga. Core stability exercises are relatively simple to do, needing little in the way of equipment, and can be easily incorporated into a cross-training program.

There are many benefits of core stability. You'll have improved balance, flexibility, and overall body stability. Your posture and strength will be better, you will decrease your risk of injury, and your sporting performance as a whole will be improved. You can do core stability exercises at home, but if you feel in need of guidance, find a class or fitness trainer to help you.

Core stability equipment

Resistance bands and exercise (stability) balls are used frequently in core stability to challenge the muscles. When selecting a ball, avoid the temptation to choose one that's too big for you. Large balls can be under-inflated and a softer ball reduces the effectiveness of the exercises. Choose a ball that's pumped-up firmly.

The ball can be used to sit or lean on when exercising and the resistance bands can be used with your arms, legs, and other muscles. If you're not used to exercise balls and are wary of losing balance, ensure exercise mats are placed around you in case you fall off. A session of about 20–25 minutes should be sufficient for beginners and you can build up as you become more proficient.

Exercise equipment

Time spent using exercise equipment can be valuable for all-round fitness and gives you the opportunity to work on specific muscles. Before using any equipment, get advice and tips from a qualified trainer; most health clubs offer this service and have someone available for advice. Wrongly used equipment could result in unnecessary injury.

The rowing machine is beneficial for exercising your quadriceps, upper body, abdominals, and lower back and can help build up stamina. Try to keep your

FINDING THE NEUTRAL POSITION

Before trying core stability, it's important to learn how to put your spine and pelvis into a neutral position.

1 Lie on your back on the floor. Use an exercise mat if necessary.

2 Put your feet flat on the floor, with your knees bent, and your legs hip-distance apart.

3 In neutral position, you will have a small curve in the lower back, so there's a small gap between your waist and the floor. If your pelvis is tilting toward or away from you, adjust your position.

back straight and let your arms, legs, and shoulders do the hard work. Machines that replicate a skiing action are great for upper body, arms, and legs. Weight training using either machines or handheld weights increases strength.

The treadmill, although another form of running, can be useful for learning to keep pace. It also provides an easy way to try uphill running—when it gets too much the hill function can be switched off!

Don't overdo your sessions or try to push yourself too much. Stay within your means and aim to exercise for 25-30 minutes per session at first. You can build up as you progress. It's fine to stick to one or two pieces of equipment if that works best for you, but if you thrive on variety, there are plenty of options to choose from.

tip Always remember to do warm-up and cool-down exercises when using exercise equipment or doing core stability exercises.

CORE STABILITY

Exercise balls provide a good way to train your core muscles, especially when you're sitting on the ball. Leg lifts will help tighten your abdominal muscles and improve movement of the pelvis, plus boost your balance and stability skills, whereas the curling exercise helps improve flexibility in the spine and is one of the best ways of exercising the rectus abdominus muscle. This muscle extends from the ribs to the pelvis and is the muscle responsible for the sought-after "six-pack."

The leg stretch works on the legs, back, hips, and abdominals and helps stretch and strengthen the key muscles used in running. The resistance band exercise will help boost the strength of your abdominal muscles, as well as stretching the spine.

RESISTANCE BAND ROLL

1 Sit on an exercise mat with your back straight. Extend your legs out in front of you, with your feet close together and your knees bent.

2 Place the resistance band around the soles of your feet and hold on to the ends.

3 Slowly tip your pelvis backward, so that you begin to roll back (*above*). Continue to move slowly, until your shoulders touch the floor.

4 Lean back into the exercise mat and relax. Repeat this exercise a second time.

LEG LIFT USING THE BALL

1 Sit upright on an exercise ball and ensure your spine is in a neutral position. Put your feet flat on the floor, about hip-distance apart. Lift your arms up and out to your sides, so they are at shoulder height.

2 Slowly lift up your right leg, while keeping the knee bent and your back straight (*above*). Don't try to lift it too high because it may disturb your balance and make you wobble.

3 Hold this position for 10 seconds, then relax. Repeat this exercise a second time, then exercise the other leg.

EXERCISE BALL CURL

1 Kneel down by the exercise ball and move your body onto it, so your shoulders and torso are balanced on the ball and your head is sticking over the far edge. Your knees should be bent and your feet should be wide apart to help with balance. Keep your arms tucked in close to the side of your body.

2 Use your abdominal muscles to curl forward and upward. As you move, stretch your arms out in front of your head (*above right*). Move slowly, so you don't wobble, and help control the movement.

3 Hold the position for 10 seconds, then relax. Repeat the exercise four times.

LEG STRETCH

1 Lie on your back on an exercise mat, with an exercise ball at your feet. You may want to place a small cushion behind your head for extra support. Ensure your back is in a neutral position, then bend your knees and rest your feet on the exercise ball. Keep your arms flat on the floor beside you.

2 Press your left leg into the ball as you raise your right leg into the air (*below*). Keep your right leg as straight as possible.

3 Hold the position for 8-10 seconds, then move your foot back down onto the ball. Repeat with your right leg. Exercise each leg four times, then relax.

tip *If the ball moves around as you put your feet on it, try propping it against a wall so it can't roll backward.*

Cycling

Cycling is a popular cross-training choice among runners and it can benefit both those who are new to the sport as well as more advanced runners. Cycling places less stress on the body than running, so you can cycle for longer than you would be able to run.

Although, like running, the main work is carried out by your legs, cycling also incorporates the use of other muscles. For example, cycling places more demands on your quads and gluteus maximus muscles than running. The added bonus is that the muscles you use regularly when running will have some rest time—perfect if they're tired and in need of recovery.

The bike you use should be comfortable, in safe working condition, and the right size for your height. There's no point in borrowing a child's bike, for example, because you'll only be uncomfortable and unable to move your legs as freely as you could on a bike designed for an adult. If you don't own a bike and don't want to buy one, just use an exercise bike at the health club.

When you first begin to incorporate cycling into your training schedule, start out slowly by doing short rides on the bike, for example 20-25 minutes at a time. As you get used to cycling and build up your cycling fitness level, you can increase the time.

Just as there are different types of running, cycling encompasses different specialities, such as mountain biking, track racing, or road racing, so there's the opportunity to try new methods and add even more interest into your training.

Swimming

Swimming is an ideal accompaniment to running because it helps to strengthen the upper body. When you're running, you predominantly use the muscles in your lower body, but when swimming, it's the upper body that plays an important role. However, swimming helps stretch the hamstrings and hips, too, and the action of moving your legs in the water can improve flexibility in your ankles.

Swimming is also one of the least stressful forms of exercise, so it's an ideal choice if your muscles are feeling stiff and sore or you are recovering from an injury. And you don't need to invest in expensive equipment. Try to swim for up to 30 minutes per session; you can increase your time in the water as fitness levels increase. Remember, you should try to balance the number of running sessions you do per week with the same number of cross-training sessions, which in this case means trips to the pool.

Some people love swimming, but for those of us who aren't natural swimmers, plodding along at the same pace can become monotonous. Thankfully, there are ways of alleviating the boredom. To provide variety, try alternating between different strokes—one lap of front crawl followed by a lap of backstroke and then butterfly. Or try speeding up your pace for one lap, then slowing down for the next.

CAUTION!

If you're new to cycling, it's important to begin slowly and not overdo it, even if you consider yourself to have a good fitness level from running. Each sport differs and requires a different set of skills and the use of a specific range of muscles, so being fit in one sport doesn't necessarily mean you'll slip with ease into another. If you haven't ridden in years, a few sessions in the health club on an exercise bike will help to get you back into it.

tip Finding someone to go swimming with can help. Whether or not your swimming partner is a runner too, you can try racing each other or just use their presence to keep you motivated.

3

Advanced Training

Now you have mastered the basics, you are ready to move to the next level. This chapter focuses on what is involved in running on different terrains, equipment you may find useful as you become more advanced, and the part played by fun runs and races in improving your performance and keeping you motivated.

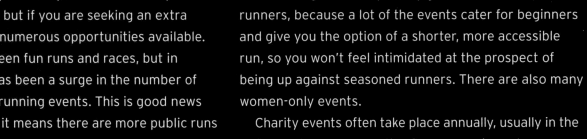

TOWN AND TRACK

Regular running for your own pleasure or to keep fit is rewarding in itself, but if you are seeking an extra challenge, there are numerous opportunities available. There have always been fun runs and races, but in recent years there has been a surge in the number of charity fund-raising running events. This is good news for runners because it means there are more public runs to choose from. It is especially good for relatively new runners, because a lot of the events cater for beginners and give you the option of a shorter, more accessible run, so you won't feel intimidated at the prospect of being up against seasoned runners. There are also many women-only events.

Charity events often take place annually, usually in the spring and summer months. Some organizers, however, try to make their event a little different and you might, for example, find yourself running at night. As well as charity runs there are fun runs, races (for example, at athletic tracks), half-marathons and marathons. A fun run can be a sensible option in the beginning.

Taking part in a race or other running event is an excellent incentive: it keeps your motivation going and gives you something to aim for. There is a real buzz to being involved in a public event and, however hard the run may be, it is a fantastic feeling to approach the finishing line and then finally cross it.

Choosing an event

When you are choosing a race to enter, assess your current running ability and don't aim too high at first. Although you may have dreams of competing in a marathon one day, it is an enormous undertaking to train for such a long race without much experience. It is wiser to be realistic at first and pick something less demanding, such as a 5,000 m (3.1 miles) or a 10,000 m (6.2 miles) event. The 5,000 m is suitable for new runners and will stretch the more experienced.

Make a shortlist of a few possible events, then find out more details of each. Consider the practicalities, such as where they are taking place, how easy it would be for

you to get there, how much it costs to take part, whether the race is aimed at beginners or if the atmosphere is likely to be highly competitive, and if there will be crowd support. If you are unsure of any aspects, phone the race organizer and ask.

Crowd support is great, because it's motivating to have people cheering you on. Plus, it means you can invite friends or family along to cheer from the sidelines and meet you at the end. Having support during the race can be beneficial, too, so why not ask a friend or someone from a running club, if you belong to one, to enter the race with you?

tip *For your very first race, pick a local event. You will find the experience less stressful if you don't have to travel a long way or stay overnight: a good night's sleep beforehand is essential and familiar surroundings will calm any pre-race nerves.*

Training

Once you've signed on the dotted line and paid your entry fee, the hard work begins. Even if you have only entered a short race and think you will cope with it easily, don't be complacent about your training. You need to keep running regularly to ensure you are in good shape and can deal with the demands of the event. Take time to plan your training sessions carefully, focusing on building up your strength and pace gradually over a number of weeks.

Include plenty of cross training, too, and try to vary what surfaces you run on. You should do this even if, for example, you know your race will be entirely run on grass, tarmac, or track, because different surfaces not only add variation to your routine, but also reduce your risk of injury (see page 24).

When you are training for a race, your sessions should include at least one run shorter than your race, one the same distance, and one longer run. For example, if you enter a 5,000 m (3.1 miles) race, your shorter distance would be 3,000 m (1.9 miles) and your longer distance 7,000 m (4.4 miles). By training in this manner you will have the confidence to know that you can do at least the amount you need to and keep going for longer, so you won't find yourself completely exhausted by the time you reach the finish line. It also gives you an incentive to choose a longer race next time, as you will know you can already go that bit further.

It is good to change the pace, so try to run your 3,000 m training run faster than you plan to run the actual race, use the same pace when you are running the 5,000 m, and a slower pace for the 7,000 m. Either do this training as straightforward runs, or use interval training to break the session into manageable chunks.

Examples of how this could work out in practice are as follows:

3,000 m (1.9 miles)

Run for 300 m (330 yd), walk for 1^1/$_2$ minutes.
Run for 300 m (330 yd), walk for 1^1/$_2$ minutes.
Run for 300 m (330 yd), walk for 1^1/$_2$ minutes.
Run for 300 m (330 yd), walk for 1^1/$_2$ minutes.
Run for 300 m (330 yd), walk for 1^1/$_2$ minutes.
Walk for 2^1/$_2$ minutes.
Run for 300 m (330 yd), walk for 1^1/$_2$ minutes.
Run for 300 m (330 yd), walk for 1^1/$_2$ minutes.
Run for 300 m (330 yd), walk for 1^1/$_2$ minutes.
Run for 300 m (330 yd), walk for 1^1/$_2$ minutes.
Run for 300 m (330 yd), walk for 1^1/$_2$ minutes.

5,000 m (3.1 miles)

Run for 1,000 m (0.6 mile), walk for 1 minute.
Run for 400 m (435 yd), walk for 1 minute.
Run for 1,000 m (0.6 mile), walk for 1 minute.
Run for 400 m (435 yd), walk for 1 minute.
Run for 1,000 m (0.6 mile), walk for 1 minute.
Run for 200 m (220 yd), walk for 1 minute.
Run for 1,000 m (0.6 mile), walk for 1 minute.

7,000 m (4.4 miles)

Run for 400 m (435 yd), walk for 1 minute.
Run for 600 m (655 yd), walk for 1 minute.
Run for 800 m (880 yd), walk for 1^1/$_2$ minutes.
Run for 1,000 m (0.6 mile), walk for 2 minutes.
Run for 800 m (880 yd), walk for 1^1/$_2$ minutes.
Run for 1,000 m (0.6 mile), walk for 2 minutes.
Run for 600 m (655 yd), walk for 1 minute.
Run for 1,000 m (0.6 mile), walk for 2 minutes.
Run for 400 m (435 yd), walk for 1 minute.
Run for 400 m (435 yd), walk for 1 minute.

WHAT TO PACK FOR A RACE

Pack your sport bag the day before and think carefully about what you will need. Leaving it until the day is always a mistake—your nerves could get the better of you and you may forget something. Follow the checklist (right): you may not need everything on the list but the absolute essentials to include are fluids, food to eat after the race, a towel, and a change of clothes.

Your race number: you won't be allowed entry without it.

Safety pins: for attaching your race number.

Running clothes: top, shorts/pants, sports bra, jacket, hat, gloves, and socks.

Light backpack to carry beverages, tissues, bandages, safety pins, and other essentials.

Large garbage bag in case you need to wrap yourself up at the end of the race.

Running shoes, plus a spare pair for emergencies.

Petroleum jelly for sore lips or other chafed areas.

Painkillers in case you need them afterward.

Warm clothes to change into after the race.

Energy drinks and snacks.

Sunglasses and sunscreen.

Music player, if you use one.

Sports watch or timer.

Water bottle.

Tissues.

Bandages.

Towel.

Training sessions in advance of longer runs work on the same principle, and the earlier you can start training, the better. That's especially so for half-marathons and marathons, because your body needs time to prepare. If you are planning on doing a 5,000 m (3.1 miles) run, training for a minimum of eight weeks should be sufficient. If you've set your sights on a 10,000 m (6.2 miles) run, then train for a minimum of ten weeks. Training for a marathon, needs at least four months.

tip Use a chart to plan your training sessions, making sure you include plenty of variety; try to team up with other runners occasionally for added motivation. You

don't want to overdo it, so include plenty of rest days, too. If you're training for a 5,000 m or 10,000 m run, then ensure you have three days of rest where you don't run at all. This way, you'll be doing a good amount of training, but won't be overdoing it.

tip Many people imagine the final half mile (1 km) is the hardest part of the race. However, the half mile before last can be just as bad. It's very easy to find yourself slowing down without realizing it, so try to make a conscious effort to speed up at this stage. This final push will help make getting around the last mile a little easier.

HILL OR MOUNTAIN RUNNING

If you want to increase the challenge when you are running, you could try hill or mountain running. These involve running on rough terrain, navigating paths, and running up what can be very demanding routes into hills or mountains.

Before you attempt hill or mountain running, it is crucial that your level of fitness is good. Even if you have achieved a time of 40-45 minutes in a 10,000 m (6.2 miles) road race, you won't necessarily be able to cope with the demands of running on the hills. This uneven terrain is far more difficult to run on than road, you will need to climb considerable heights, and the weather can significantly affect conditions.

One way to test your own fitness beforehand is by practising running up and down a hill. Ideally, choose a hill that's no more than 435 yards (400 m) in distance and not too steep—you should be able to see the top from the bottom. Run up the hill, leaning into it as you go. If you're out of breath by the time you get to the top, stop and rest. Either walk or jog back down. If you can manage to run up the hill up to five times in one session, then it's a good indication that you may be able to cope with hill running.

Although this type of running is possible on your own, it is advisable to join a group at first, because experienced rough-terrain runners will have valuable tips to pass on. It is also recommended from a safety point of view, because hills and mountains pose extra risks that are better faced as a group.

tip *If you are running alone, take a cell phone and let someone at home or a family member know where you are going to be, in case an unexpected situation or emergency arises.*

COMMON PROBLEMS

Hills and mountains carry risks, even for proficient runners. Common complaints are:

Soreness in the lower back—usually caused by leaning too far forward as you are running up or downhill.

Breathing too rapidly—usually caused by trying to run too fast or over-striding. It's a common issue when running uphill, but you don't want your breathing and heart rate to accelerate too quickly. It's hard, but you need to try to control your breathing and take deep breaths instead of shallow ones, because this will help your uphill running ability.

Sore hamstring muscles—usually caused by over-striding, so concentrate on your pace and try to maintain even strides.

Sore shoulders and arm muscles—often related to uphill running position, so be careful not to swing your arms or extend them too far forward.

Loss of rhythm—a common scenario, especially when running downhill. Try to maintain yours by sticking to the same pace and resisting the urge to charge on the way down.

Sore or painful quadriceps—often caused by having to brake too much when running downhill, which makes your quads work extra hard.

The benefits

Although tough and demanding, uphill running can be very good for you. It exercises many of your key muscles, strengthening them in much the same way as strength-training exercises in a health club–only, in this case, you are not performing individual exercises on isolated areas, but taking a full-body approach. Over time, you will notice improvements in your muscle power, particularly the strength of your legs, and you will be able to run faster when training on roads and other flatter surfaces. The demands of running up hills will also give an additional boost to your cardiovascular system, which will make you feel healthier in general.

Events

Hill running is a popular sport and various hill and mountain running events are held regularly in many countries, catering for a range of experience. Some races involve only a single gentle hill and take a couple of hours, while others extend over several days and involve far more challenging terrain. These events are not just about running–you will need to navigate your way up and around the hills, too. In some instances, a route will be provided, but at other times it adds more to the experience for you to do this yourself.

tip A well-developed sense of direction and an ability to read maps are valuable skills when hill running. For extra help, you might want to invest in a Global Positioning System, or GPS (see page 81).

CROSS-COUNTRY RUNNING

If hills and mountains are not for you, but you nevertheless want to try different terrains and explore the great outdoors, cross-country running is an option. You could still find yourself having to run uphill and the areas you run in may be rough underfoot, but the inclines won't be as demanding.

There is nothing to stop you trying cross-country running of your own accord—although you should always tell someone where you are going if you are on your own. However, one of the benefits of this type of running is that you can also take part in events as a member of a team, competing together. Cross-country running has a long history and is a well-recognized sport. For those who find race running as an individual an isolating experience, it can come as a relief to run as a team member. There is still plenty of opportunity to challenge yourself and achieve a personal best, or beat any previous standards set.

Cross-country terrain varies, but may include tarmac roads, dirt tracks, grass, wooded areas, hills and uneven ground. The unpredictability, coupled with potentially adverse weather conditions, can make the course difficult. If the weather is wet, for example, the ground underfoot can quickly deteriorate into a series of muddy puddles. Some runners thrive on this, enjoying the fact that they don't know what they will have to face next.

As with hill running, knowing how to read a map and use a compass, or program a GPS device, is very useful when running cross-country, especially if you are out training on your own. At events you will usually be guided and follow an established course, but a map can be useful back-up.

tip *Most cross-country races tend to be scheduled for the winter months, from about October to March. They include important national and international championships as well as regional events.*

Training

Because the terrain you will be running on will be uneven, it is important that you build up the length of time for which you can run. When you are running on ground that is neither flat nor predictable, it can take longer to cover distances than it would if you were, say, road running. You may be able to run 5,000 m (3.1 miles) easily on a flat surface, but covering the same distance across country will demand more from you.

Bear this in mind when you are considering whether to sign up for an event. It is better to start cautiously and then build up your distances as you become more confident. You will achieve a great feeling of satisfaction when you complete the course, and won't be deterred from ever taking part again—which could happen if you enter a race that is beyond your current abilities.

Include plenty of different surfaces in your training plan and run routes of varying lengths and difficulty. Try to find circular routes, so you don't have to turn back on yourself. Incorporate cross training, such as cycling and walking, into your schedule, too, because they both help strengthen muscles and increase stamina.

Running outside in bad weather may help prepare you for adverse weather conditions on event days, but if it flies in the face of common sense to venture outdoors, you can still gain plenty of benefits from using exercise equipment in your training. For example, on a treadmill, warm up with about 10 minutes of gentle jogging, then set the hill gradient to 1 percent. If you know your usual running speed for a 10,000 m (6.2 miles) race, set the speed function to about 15 seconds slower. Run on the treadmill at this pace for 5 minutes, before upping the gradient to 5 percent. If you're using the treadmill regularly, you can slowly increase the gradient during each training session and build up your hill running ability.

tip *Look out for hazards when you run on uneven ground, such as exposed tree roots or loose stones —you don't want to trip or stumble on them and risk injuring yourself. Most runners find they adapt easily to keeping an eye on the path in front of them.*

ADVANCED RUNNING

As a regular runner, you need to be aware of the surfaces you cover and the degree of shock absorption they provide. A good pair of running shoes will give some protection against hard surfaces, but if you are running regularly on hard areas, it is bound to have some effect. Each time your feet hit the ground, the impact is felt by the rest of your body. If it is a surface that absorbs shock, the shock to your body will be limited. But hard surfaces, such as concrete, offer no shock absorption at all, so your body bears the brunt. Over time, bone, cartilage, and muscle will develop wear and tear, leaving you prone to injury.

The risk is increased if you run on exactly the same surface without varying your routine at all. Although it is good to develop habits and running in the same conditions may work well for you, incorporating runs on other surfaces will vary the impact felt by your body, as well as provide variety.

Advanced training techniques

If your goal is to run faster, you need to incorporate some speed work into your training.

Fartlek (Swedish for speed play) is a good speed-work technique for beginners because it's easy to do and can be incorporated into any of your usual runs. Try it when running on trails or grass. The idea is that you combine spurts of fast and hard running with gentle running. You can practice fartlek when you want and as hard as you want—there are no set rules—but it is convenient to aim for fast bursts between certain markers, such as trees or benches.

Fartlek combines interval work with continuous running and allows you to have short bursts where you run a bit faster. Practicing this technique will come in handy when you're taking part in races, because you'll already have experience of suddenly running a little faster when you need to.

Interval work involves short bursts of very fast sprinting for between 30 seconds and 3 minutes at a time, followed by gentle jogging to recover. This helps improve the way your body uses oxygen, but is a technique only recommended for intermediate and advanced runners. Although similar to fartlek, with interval training you run at a faster and higher intensity, which is why it's advised that only intermediate and advanced runners try it.

RUNNING SURFACES

Concrete: the most unyielding surface for runners. Avoid where possible.

Tarmac: slightly better than concrete, but still not ideal.

Grass: flat, firm, and trimmed grass is kind to the body.

Trails or dirt paths: a good option, because usually soft. Watch out for exposed tree roots.

Sand: flat and firm sand is good. Avoid soft and uneven sand, because it can lead to calf strain.

Track: specially made running tracks are ideal. They absorb shock and provide perfect conditions.

Advanced equipment

As you progress with your running, it may be useful to invest in some more advanced forms of equipment. A pedometer, for example, will calculate the exact distance of your run. They are easy to use and clip onto the waistband of your shorts or pants. Many models also record the number of steps you have taken, your speed, and the number of calories burned. To ensure accuracy, you first have to set it up by inputting your stride length.

If you are planning a lot of hill or cross-country running, a Global Positioning System (GPS) device is recommended. This handy piece of equipment uses satellite technology to determine your position and will help guide you to your destination. A range of models is available, including small devices that can be clipped on your waistband, tucked in a pocket, or worn on your wrist. As well as helping with map positions, a GPS can measure distance, average speed, and elevation.

If you enjoy listening to music as you train, look for portable music players that can synchronize with specially designed shoes with built-in sensors to track your run.

4

A Training Program

Whatever your running ability, you will see great improvements with regular training. Start by setting a training program: it will ensure that you get the best from your running and also keep you focused and motivated. This chapter includes sample programs for both beginners and intermediates, which you can use as a basis from which to develop a schedule that works for you.

HOW TO PLAN A RUNNING PROGRAM

You have made great progress already, and now it is time to build on those foundations. Developing, and sticking to, a regular running program will not only maintain your motivation, but will also ensure that your level of fitness doesn't waver through lack of practice. By planning your program in advance, you can also be sure that you get a good balance of exercise throughout the week.

You also need to be realistic: there will inevitably be

times when you cannot run as regularly as you would like, perhaps because of an important work project or family commitments. In these periods, don't expect progress, but do what you can to try to keep up the momentum. If you simply abandon your program, your level of ability will decline, and this will make things a lot harder when you start running again.

Before you work out your schedule, assess your current level of fitness, what you want to achieve, and how long you've got to do it. Don't be tempted to train intensely for too short a time, because you are likely to pay for it. For example, if your aim is to compete in a half-marathon (13.1 miles/21 km), it's advisable first of all to be able to run at least 10 km (6.2 miles). You should then give yourself at least two months in which to train. Similarly, if you want to run a full marathon (26.2 miles/42.2 km), you'll need a minimum of four months in order to get up to standard.

Your schedule should be clearly written or typed up, either as a list or in chart format, and placed somewhere that you will see regularly, such as on the door of the refrigerator. That way you can see at a glance what you are intending to do and exactly when you will be doing it. Don't forget to include time for a thorough warm-up and cool-down each time you exercise, and to balance your running with cross training.

Using the sample programs

The sample training programs set out in the following pages are intended for use as guides for runners of varying abilities. The first is designed for new runners who have completed the schedule set out in Your First Run (see page 32) and are ready for advancement. It

takes a gentle, gradual approach, but you will build up your running ability over a number of weeks. The subsequent programs are for runners at an intermediate level, who want to train for a 5,000 m (3.1 miles) or a 10,000 m (6.2 miles) run, or even for a marathon.

If, for any reason, the sample programs don't suit you, or you would like more specialized advice on what to include in a tailored plan, it is advisable to seek help from a professional. A personal trainer, your local health club, or a running club are all good sources of information. If you are a member of a running club, you may also want to join in its training sessions, which are often organized to prepare members for particular events. Fellow members will be able to give you suggestions on training, and you will benefit from training alongside runners at a similar level who are trying to achieve similar aims.

tip *It's important to include rest days in your schedule, when you don't do any running but can use this time to enjoy other gentler forms of exercise. Ideally, rest days shouldn't be back-to-back, but spaced throughout the week. For example, if you're training for a 5,000 m or 10,000 m race, aim for three rest days per week.*

Second run and beyond

This training program follows on from Your First Run (see page 32), the schedule for beginners that was set in the Getting Started chapter. It will take you from 20 minutes nonstop running to 30 minutes.

The training program follows a ten-week structure. As before, you progress slowly but surely, building on your 20-minute running ability and gradually incorporating slightly longer runs. Most weeks include a combination of running with short bursts of brisk walking, although in the latter stages this alternates from one week to the next. With this approach, you won't be running for more than 20 minutes for a few weeks to enable you to be fully comfortable with that level of running before you move on. Beginners should find the schedule easy to work with, but if you find any one week more difficult than the others, repeat the training for that week before moving on to the next week.

This plan should ideally be completed two or three times a week. Before each run, remember to warm up properly and cool down afterward. If once you embark on the plan, it seems too easy, skip the first few weeks and start your training at week four. You should only do this if you feel completely at ease with running 20 minutes nonstop and have been successfully doing so for a while. Although it can be tempting to skip stages, this is not advisable in the long term. It is better to start at the beginning and work your way up gradually, than to skip a few weeks and find you can't maintain the pace.

SECOND RUN PROGRAM

Week	Plan
1	Run for 10 minutes, walk for 1½ minutes Run for 10 minutes, walk for 1½ minutes
2	Run for 12 minutes, walk for 1 minute Run for 8 minutes, walk for 1 minute
3	Run for 15 minutes, walk for 1 minute Run for 5 minutes, walk for 1 minute
4	Run for 20 minutes nonstop
5	Run for 20 minutes, walk for 1½ minutes Run for 5 minutes, walk for 1½ minutes
6	Run for 25 minutes nonstop
7	Run for 25 minutes, walk for 1 minute Run for 3 minutes, walk for 1 minute
8	Run for 28 minutes nonstop
9	Run for 28 minutes, walk for 1 minute Run for 2 minutes, walk for 1 minute
10	Run for 30 minutes nonstop

Once you have reached week 10 and can run for 30 minutes nonstop, you need to retain this level of running.

5,000 m training program

This 5,000 m (3.1 miles) training plan is aimed at runners who have completed the Second Run and Beyond program (see page 86) and can now run for 30 minutes nonstop several times a week.

It can be used alongside the method described in Chapter 3, Advanced Training (see pages 74–5), on preparing yourself to run 3,000 m (1.9 miles), 5,000 m and 7,000 m (4.4 miles) distances, so you know you can cope with a longer distance than you will run in the race.

This schedule can be adapted to fit in with existing commitments and you can alter your rest days if necessary. They can also be used for other forms of gentle exercise and offer a good opportunity to carry out cross-training exercises, such as cycling or swimming.

5,000 M TRAINING PROGRAM

Week	Mon	Tues	Wed	Thurs	Fri	Sat	Sun
1	Run for 20 minutes	Rest	Fartlek or cross training	Rest	Run for 20 minutes	Rest	Run for 30 minutes
2	Run for 20 minutes	Rest	Fartlek or cross training	Rest	Run for 20 minutes	Rest	Run for 35 minutes
3	Run for 25 minutes	Rest	Fartlek or cross training	Rest	Run for 25 minutes	Rest	Run for 30 minutes
4	Run for 25 minutes	Rest	Fartlek or cross training	Rest	Run for 30 minutes	Rest	Run for 35 minutes
5	Run for 30 minutes	Rest	Fartlek or cross training	Rest	Run for 35 minutes	Rest	Run for 40 minutes
6	Run for 35 minutes	Rest	Fartlek or cross training	Rest	Run for 40 minutes	Rest	Run for 30 minutes
7	Run for 40 minutes	Rest	Fartlek or cross training	Rest	Run for 35 minutes	Rest	Run for 25 minutes
8	Run for 30 minutes	Rest	Fartlek or cross training	Rest	Run for 35 minutes	Rest	Run for 25 minutes

10,000 m training program

This program makes the move from running in terms of minutes to running in terms of distance (10,000 m is the equivalent of just over six miles). You may find it useful to take a pedometer with you on your runs to find out how long it takes you to complete an established distance. Then you can work out a rough estimate of how long it will take to run further.

In the first few weeks of the program, you will be concentrating on building up your stamina so that you can run for up to four miles (6.4 km) per session. The latter weeks then add in more elements, which will help improve your strength. You'll notice that the program builds you up to run more than 10,000 m (6.2 miles), so when the time for race day arrives, you should be able to cope well with the distance. It also gives you a good starting point for subsequent training programs, if you want to run further.

DISTANCE CONVERSIONS

1 km = 0.6 mile	1 mile = 1.6 km
2 km = 1.2 miles	2 miles = 3.2 km
3 km = 1.9 miles	3 miles = 4.8 km
4 km = 2.5 miles	4 miles = 6.4 km
5 km = 3.1 miles	5 miles = 8.0 km
6 km = 3.7 miles	6 miles = 9.7 km
7 km = 4.4 miles	7 miles = 11.3 km
8 km = 5.0 miles	8 miles = 12.9 km
9 km = 5.6 miles	9 miles = 14.5 km
10 km = 6.2 miles	10 miles = 16.0 km

10,000 M TRAINING PROGRAM

Week	Mon	Tues	Wed	Thurs	Fri	Sat	Sun	Total km
1	Run 3 km	Rest	Run 5 km	Rest	Run 5 km	Rest	Run 6 km	19
2	Run 5 km	Rest	Run 5 km	Rest	Run 6 km	Rest	Run 5 km	21
3	Run 5 km	Rest	Run 3 km; do 1.5 km of fartlek work; run 1.5 km	Rest	Run 6 km	Rest	Run 5 km	22
4	Run 5 km	Rest	Run 3 km; do 2 km of fartlek work; run 3 km	Rest	Run 6 km	Rest	Run 6 km	25
5	Run 5 km	Rest	Run 3 km; do 2 km of fartlek work; run 3 km	Rest	Run 6 km	Rest	Run 6 km	25
6	Run 5 km	Rest	Run 3 km; do 2 km of fartlek work; run 3 km	Rest	Run 6 km	Rest	Run 8 km	27
7	Run 6 km	Rest	Run 3 km; do 2 km of fartlek work; run 3 km	Rest	Run 6 km	Rest	Run 7 km	27
8	Run 6 km	Rest	Run 3 km; do 2 km of fartlek work; run 3 km	Rest	Run 6 km	Rest	Run 8 km	28
9	Run 6 km	Rest	Run 3 km; do 2 km of fartlek work; run 3 km	Rest	Run 8 km	Rest	Run 8 km	30
10	Run 6 km	Rest	Run 2 km; do 2 km of fartlek work; run 2 km	Rest	Run 10 km	Rest	Run 8 km	30
Race Week	Run 6 km	Rest	Run 3 km	Rest	Run 3 km	Rest	Run the 10,000 m race	22

Marathon training program

Running a marathon (26.2 miles/42.2 km) is the ultimate dream of many beginners, but it can seem extremely far away when you are starting out. However, it's not an unattainable dream, and if you have progressed through the other training programs and have completed a 10,000 m (6.2 miles) race, you have a good chance of successfully taking part in a marathon.

Before you attempt this schedule, you should have been running a distance of about 15 miles (24 km) to 20 miles (32 km) a week for at least one month. If you have worked your way up and completed the previous training programs, you should have arrived naturally at this level of fitness.

The program is spread over a four-month, or 16-week, period and slowly builds up the number of days per week you run. Whereas in previous

programs you ran on a Monday, in this plan Monday becomes a rest day and you run more on the weekend. However, this program is only a guide, so if it doesn't work for you, play around with it to suit your time availability.

Once you have completed your four-month schedule, you should be prepared for the race-week program. You need to keep running, but shouldn't attempt as long a run in the days before your marathon as in previous weeks. Obviously, you don't want to be worn out before the race.

If you have completed the four-month training and you still have a few more weeks to go before the marathon, then continue repeating the four-weeks' training from the last month to maintain your level of fitness. Switch to the race-week schedule in the final run-up to the event.

MARATHON TRAINING PROGRAM

Week	Mon	Tues	Wed	Thurs	Fri	Sat	Sun	Total km
Month 1								
1	Rest	Run 5 km	Rest	Run 5 km	Rest	Run 9 km	Run 5 km	24
2	Rest	Run 5 km	Rest	Run 6 km	Rest	Run 9 km	Run 5 km	25
3	Rest	Run 5 km	Rest	Run 6 km	Rest	Run 9 km	Run 6 km	26
4	Rest	Run 5 km	Rest	Run 6 km	Rest	Run 11 km	Run 8 km	30
Month 2								
1	Rest	Run 6 km	Rest	Run 6 km	Rest	Run 11 km	Run 8 km	31
2	Rest	Run 6 km	Rest	Run 6 km	Rest	Run 13 km	Run 8 km	33
3	Rest	Run 6 km	Rest	Run 6 km	Rest	Run 14 km	Run 8 km	34
4	Rest	Run 6 km	Rest	Run 6 km	Rest	Run 16 km	Run 8 km	36
Month 3								
1	Rest	Run 5 km	Run 6 km	Run 5 km	Rest	Run 19 km	Run 5 km	40
2	Rest	Run 5 km	Run 6 km	Run 6 km	Rest	Run 19 km	Run 5 km	41
3	Rest	Run 5 km	Run 6 km	Run 6 km	Rest	Run 26 km	Run 5 km	48
4	Rest	Run 5 km	Run 6 km	Run 6 km	Rest	Run 29 km	Run 5 km	51
Month 4								
1	Rest	Run 5 km	Run 6 km	Run 6 km	Rest	Run 32 km	Run 5 km	54
2	Rest	Run 6 km	Run 5 km	Run 6 km	Rest	Run 32 km	Run 5 km	54
3	Rest	Run 5 km	Run 6 km	Run 6 km	Rest	Run 26 km	Run 5 km	48
4	Rest	Run 5 km	Run 6 km	Run 6 km	Rest	Run 19 km	Run 5 km	41
Race Week								
	Rest	Run 6 km	Run 6 km	Run 6 km	Rest	Run 3 km	Run the marathon	63.2

GLOSSARY

Abdominals A term used to describe the stomach muscles.

Bleep Test A test that is often used to determine fitness levels. It involves running between two points to a series of audible bleeps; as the interval between bleeps reduces, you are forced to increase your speed.

Cool-down A period at the end of your running schedule where you carry out gentle jogging and stretching exercises. This helps slowly return your body, and your heart rate, to its resting state.

Core Muscles The deep postural muscles that form the core of the body. These muscles help you to achieve a good posture, and core stability exercises can be used to strengthen them.

Cross Training The practice of incorporating a range of other forms of exercise, such as swimming or cycling, with running. This enables you to work on other muscles and reduce the risk of injuries occurring. It also provides a change of scene so that you don't get bored with only running.

Endorphins Chemicals that occur naturally in the pituitary gland at the base of the spine. Released when you exercise, they are known for improving mood and well-being and for dulling pain. The feeling of well-being that's produced from running is sometimes referred to as the "runner's high."

Fartlek The Swedish for "speed play", this is a technique involving unstructured speed training. The runner varies their speed as they run, for varying amounts of time. It's good for working on speed, and it helps provide a different element to your running routine.

Global Positioning System (GPS) A satellite tracking gadget that can be used to identify your current map position and your target route. Some devices can also calculate speed and running pace. It's particularly useful for hill, mountain, and cross-country running.

Gluteus Maximus The strongest muscle in the body, covering a large part of the buttock. Together with the hamstring muscle, it is used when you extend your legs behind your body.

Hamstring Muscles The group of muscles located at the back of the thigh, which bend the knee and extend the hips.

Heart Rate Monitor (HRM) A piece of equipment that measures heart rate. It usually consists of a strap with sensors that's worn across the chest and a small receiver, which is worn on the wrist. Some models also incorporate a watch.

Iliotibial Band A thick band of tissue that goes from the knee joint to the pelvis. Iliotibial Band Syndrome (ITBS) is a common thigh injury generally associated with running.

Interval Training A type of training technique that is used to improve speed and overall fitness. It involves running at a fast pace for a set distance or number of minutes, followed by a recovery period of walking, resting, or gentle jogging

Maximum Heart Rate (MHR) A term that refers to the maximum number of times the heart can beat in one minute. It's possible to work out your own approximate MHR by deducting your age from 220 (men) or 226 (women).

Normal Pronator A term used to describe a runner who lands on the outside of their heel, rolls slightly inward then pushes off again on the ball of their foot and their toes. A normal pronator will probably have feet with medium arches.

Orthotics Special foot-supporting devices or insoles for running shoes, which are often made especially for an individual. They fit inside the shoe and help to correct foot position and running motion.

Overpronator The term used to describe a runner whose foot lands on the outer side of the heel, then rolls inward, or pronates, before pushing off on the ball of their feet and their toes. An overpronator will probably have feet with low arches.

Over-Training A situation where a runner trains too hard or too much. This can result in injury, exhaustion or impaired performance. The best solution is a reduction in the amount of training or complete rest.

Pace Beeper A portable device that emits a beep. It's used by runners to help develop and improve their pace when running.

Pedometer A portable gadget that measures the distance you've run, the number of steps you've taken, your speed, and, often, the number of calories you've burned.

Quadriceps The group of muscles at the front of the thighs. Important in running, they are powerful extensors of the knee joint and also act as flexors of the hip.

Resting Heart Rate (RHR) The number of beats made by your heart per minute when you're resting. The average resting heart rate for adults lies between 60 and 80 beats per minute. The fitter you become, the lower your resting heart rate will be.

Stability Ball A large rubber ball that is used to perform exercises, particularly to strengthen the core muscles. The instability of the ball means your body has to engage many muscles to remain balanced while exercising.

Supinator The term used to describe a runner who lands on the outside of their heel, but doesn't roll in enough before pushing off again. A supinator will probably have feet with high arches.

Treadmill A piece of running equipment commonly found in a health club. It features various options that mimic conditions, such as running on a flat road or uphill, and helps you improve your running speed. Many treadmills have preset programs that you can complete.

Warm-Up An essential schedule of gentle exercise that is carried out before you begin running. It helps warm up your muscles, increase your body temperature, improve your heart rate and blood pressure, and generally prepare you for the exercise that lies ahead.

Wicking The process whereby moisture or sweat is taken away from your body and passed through a fabric. It collects on the outside of the fabric and then evaporates, rather than being absorbed. Certain breathable synthetic fabrics, such as polyester/cotton and nylon/lycra, have a wicking ability.

INDEX

The publisher would like
to thank the following for
permission to reproduce
copyright material:
Corbis: 6 A. Inden, 10
Pete Saloutos, 17 Duncan
Smith, 23 Ken Ridding, 57
Rolf Bruderer, 69 Duomo,
81 Michael Kevin Daly, 87
Comstock Select, 88 Patrik
Giardino, 90 Ben Welsh,
92 Michael Kim; **Getty**: 2
Chase Jarvis, 4 Joe Drivas,
7 Dirk Anschutz, 11 Donald
Miralle, 12 Greg Wood, 13
David Madison, 19 Gary
John Norman, 24 Stockbyte,
31 George Doyle, 33 Per
Breiehagen, 36 Janie Airey,
39 Yellow Dog Productions,
51, 72 Romilly Lockyer, 73
Stewart Cohen, 77 Fredrik
Broman, 78 Alistair Berg, 79
Dirk Anschutz, 82 Stockbyte,
84 Mark Douet; **Istock**: 8
Stephen Strathdee, 14 Heidi
Kristensen, 16 Francisco
Orellana, 21, 26 Gary Allard,
35 Myles Dumas, 40 Mario
Savoia, 41 Christine Glade, 49
Stephen Zabel, 50 Wolfgang
Amri, 63 Mario Savoia, 65
Sandra O'Claire, 70 Mills
Rymer, 89 Bill Grove.